NO TURNING BACK
A Journey into the
World of Alzheimer's
With my Mother

Written and Designed
By Lyn H. Silberman

123300

A PORTION OF THE SALES OF THIS BOOK WILL BE DONATED TO THE
ALZHEIMER'S ASSOCIATION.

ADDITIONAL COPIES CAN BE ORDERED BY CALLING: 561-540-4552.

FIRST PAPERBACK EDITION: OCTOBER, 2004
PUBLISHED BY SILBERMAN ENTERPRISES, INC.
1180 LANDS END ROAD
LANTANA, FL 33462

No Turning Back:
A Journey into the World of Alzheimer's with My Mother

Table of Contents

Introduction

No Turning Back: A Journey Into the World of Alzheimer's With My Mother is a refection of that special bond between mother and daughter. It flows from this commonality into the uniquely personal story of Lyn and her mother, Ruth, on their journey of living with Alzheimer's disease for over six years. Lyn's choice to print this book in all capitals was symbolic of entering this "other world" of dementia or, as Lyn says, "Feeling lost on the road". The road theme was particularly appropriate for Lyn as it reflected the many trips she and her mother had shared together.

I remember when I first met Lyn and Ruth, not long after Ruth's diagnosis. I saw the special love and connection overlaid by a pressing fear, like luggage chained to your wrist.

Over the years I was struck by Lyn's fortitude in enabling her mother to live as independently as possible. It is hard to live with risk.

There is honesty in this work, an unveiling of the anger and guilt inherent in this journey. There is a wealth of no-nonsense, practical guidance. What will surprise the reader is the unexpected growth in Ruth's ability to show love.

If you are a daughter caring for your mother, I think you will find this journey compelling and helpful. May doors open as you seek the help you will need - as this can be a long journey – and may you be especially kind to yourself along the way.

Written by Sally Ollerton, LSW
Alzheimer's Association Cleveland Area Chapter
June 2004

Dedication

My first thank-you goes to my Mother who had the dignity to allow me the honor and privilege of caring for her during her journey into the world of Alzheimer's. I dedicate this book to her with much love.

I wish to thank my cousin and dear friend Patricia Brown for volunteering to be my first editor. She gave me invaluable feedback and encouraged me to continue writing.

My dear friend Janie Kaiser, who has been a part of my life since elementary school, was kind enough to look at the manuscript many months later and she made wonderful suggestions and forced me to question why I included some stories and not others. She helped to make this a better book.

And then there is Sally Ollerton without whom I could never have completed this book. She was there from the beginning when I mentioned I was going to try to get this all down on paper. She was my backbone throughout the process and in the end she helped me with all the chapter titles and was kind enough to write the introduction.

My friend Fredda Butowsky gave me excellent advice about changing "my mother" to "mother", which changed the emotion of the book, and for that I am grateful.

I thank my boyfriend, Ronnie Rivchun, for always being there to lean on while I was going through my journey, and my very good friends Karen Schenkel and Barbara Robbins for being such good friends throughout the journey. I could not have done any of this without their love and support.

Most of all I want to thank the families who will read this. As I say in the book "I wish you a safe journey"

Lyn H. Silberman
June 2004

NO TURNING BACK: A JOURNEY INTO THE WORLD OF ALZHEIMER'S WITH MY MOTHER

FORWARD

A WALK IN THE WOODS BY BILL BRYSON, PAGE 225
"PRESUMABLY, A CONFUSED PERSON WOULD BE TOO ADDLED TO RECOGNIZE THAT HE IS CONFUSED. ERGO, IF YOU KNOW THAT YOU ARE NOT CONFUSED THEN YOU ARE NOT CONFUSED. UNLESS, IT SUDDENLY OCCURRED TO ME – AND HERE WAS AN ARRESTING NOTION – UNLESS PERSUADING YOURSELF THAT YOU ARE NOT CONFUSED IS MERELY A CRUEL, EARLY SYMPTOM OF CONFUSION. OR EVEN AN ADVANCED SYMPTOM. WHO COULD TELL?....THAT'S THE TROUBLE WITH LOSING YOUR MIND; BY THE TIME IT'S GONE, IT'S TOO LATE TO GET IT BACK."

IN WRITING THIS STORY I WAS HOPING TO RECAPTURE THE MOTHER I HAD BEFORE HER JOURNEY INTO THE WORLD OF ALZHEIMER'S. THIS DID NOT HAPPEN. THE JOURNEY WAS TOO CONSUMING AND I LOST PARTS OF THAT MOTHER. FRIENDS OF MINE WHO HAVE READ THIS BOOK HAVE COMMENTED THAT THEY, TOO, WOULD HAVE LIKED TO KNOW MORE ABOUT MY MOTHER PRIOR TO THE ALZHEIMER'S. TO THE READERS THAT ALSO WISH THIS, I APOLOGIZE. IT'S BEYOND MY GRASP FOR NOW.

THE PURPOSE IN WRITING THIS STORY WAS NOT TO SHARE MY MOTHER WITH THE READER. RATHER IT WAS TO HELP ANY OF YOU THAT ARE ALSO GOING THROUGH THIS JOURNEY INTO THE WORLD OF ALZHEIMER'S. IF YOU HAVE ONE DECISION MADE EASIER BECAUSE OF SOMETHING YOU READ IN MY MOTHER'S STORY, I WILL CONSIDER THIS BOOK A SUCCESS.

CHAPTER ONE
A JOURNEY UNANTICIPATED

I FOUND OUT ONLY LATER THAT SHE WAS GOING TO TAKE ME PLACES I DID NOT KNOW EVEN EXISTED.

WE WERE IN LAOS. IT WAS HOT AND WE HAD SPENT HOURS GETTING THERE FROM CLEVELAND, OHIO. WHEN MOTHER ASKED OUR GUIDE "WHEN IS THE RAINY SEASON?" IT SEEMED A REASONABLE QUESTION. AT LEAST THE FIRST TIME SHE ASKED IT.

I LOST COUNT OF THE NUMBER OF TIMES MOTHER ASKED THIS QUESTION. EACH TIME, HOWEVER, IT WAS IDENTICAL. " WHEN IS THE RAINY SEASON?" ANSWER, ANOTHER QUESTION: " HOW LONG DOES IT LAST?" ANOTHER ANSWER.

AFTER THE FIRST FEW TIMES I STARTED PAYING ATTENTION. WHY WAS MOTHER ASKING THIS QUESTION ALL THE TIME? SOMETIMES SHE WOULD ASK IT JUST A FEW MINUTES AFTER SHE HAD JUST ASKED IT. SOMETIMES IT WOULD BE HOURS LATER. BUT IT WAS ALWAYS THE SAME. THE GUIDE WAS REMARKABLY PATIENT; I WAS NOT.

IN LOOKING AT THIS WEEKS LATER, I KNOW THIS WAS MY FIRST SIGNAL OF SOMETHING BEING WRONG. AT THE TIME I HAD NO IDEA HOW WRONG THINGS WOULD GET OR EVEN WHAT COULD BE WRONG. WHEN I FINALLY APPROACHED MOTHER ABOUT IT SHE SAID SHE THOUGHT SHE WAS JUST NOT HEARING THE GUIDE'S ANSWERS. THIS WOULD HAVE MADE SENSE IF SHE HAD NOT REPLIED IN FULL SENTENCES BACK TO HIM. I DID NOT POINT THAT OUT TO HER. INSTEAD I SUGGESTED SHE HAVE A HEARING TEST WHEN WE RETURNED HOME.

THERE WERE OTHER SIGNS AS WELL. MOTHER AND I HAD TRAVELLED TOGETHER MANY TIMES TO THIS PART OF THE WORLD AS WELL AS OTHER PLACES. I FOUND OUT ONLY LATER THAT SHE WAS GOING TO TAKE ME PLACES I DID NOT KNOW EVEN EXISTED. I KNEW HOW MOTHER FUNCTIONED ON A TRIP. YET THIS TRIP WAS DIFFERENT. SHE COULD NEVER REMEMBER WHERE OUR HOTEL ROOM WAS OR EVEN WHAT FLOOR IT WAS ON. SHE HAD ALWAYS BEEN IN CHARGE OF OUR TICKETS AND PAPERS. NOW I SUGGESTED THAT I TAKE CARE OF THEM FOR US. WHILE SHE WAS NOT

HAPPY ABOUT TURNING OVER THIS RESPONSIBILITY TO ME, SHE AGREED TO LET ME HAVE THE TICKETS. SHE KEPT LOSING TRACK OF HER LUGGAGE AND HOW MANY PIECES OF LUGGAGE SHE HAD. THE NORMAL FUNCTIONS OF TRAVELING WERE NO LONGER NORMAL.

I ADMIT THAT I WAS NOT AT ALL PATIENT OR UNDERSTANDING AT THE TIME. I HAD NO IDEA WHAT WAS GOING ON. WE HAD SEVERAL SMALL ALTERCATIONS BECAUSE OF THIS. BY THE TIME WE ARRIVED IN BANGKOK, WHERE WE HAD BEEN THREE OR FOUR TIMES BEFORE, NEITHER OF US WAS HAPPY WITH THE OTHER. WE WERE MEETING MY COUSIN MARGIE THERE FOR A TRAVEL AGENTS CONVENTION. WE HAD ATTENDED THESE MEETINGS BEFORE AND HAD A ROUTINE ESTABLISHED.

BEFORE WE ATTENDED ANY MEETINGS, MARGIE APPROACHED ME AND ASKED ME WHAT I HAD DONE TO MOTHER. SHE HAD COMPLAINED TO MARGIE THAT I WAS BEING MEAN AND UNKIND. I WAS NOT SURE HOW TO REPLY. I KNEW I HAD BEEN IMPATIENT AND CONCERNED. I DID NOT THINK I HAD BEEN MEAN. I EXPLAINED TO MARGIE AS BEST I COULD WHAT HAD HAPPENED IN LAOS AND WONDERED OUTLOUD IF SOMETHING WAS WRONG WITH MOTHER'S MEMORY. MARGIE AGREED TO PAY MORE ATTENTION THAN USUAL TO WHAT MOTHER DID AND SAID, AND LATER APOLOGIZED TO ME THAT SHE HAD ACCUSED ME OF BEING MEAN. SHE, TOO, WAS NOW AWARE OF SOMETHING NOT BEING QUITE RIGHT WITH MOTHER.

FROM THAT POINT ON I WAS ABLE TO BE A LITTLE MORE PATIENT WITH MOTHER, EVEN THOUGH I STILL HAD NO REAL IDEA OF THE PROBLEM. WE CONTINUED OUR TRIP TO BRUNEI AND THEN ON TO HONG KONG.

MOTHER'S VERY FAVORITE PLACE IN THE WORLD WAS HONG KONG. SHE LOVED THE BRIGHT LIGHTS OF THE HARBOR AND THE EXCITEMENT OF THE CITY. SHE HAD BEEN THERE SEVERAL TIMES; I HAD BEEN THERE AT LEAST FIVE OR SIX TIMES WITH HER. IT WAS AN INTERESTING TIME TO BE THERE FOR IN A FEW MONTHS CHINA WAS GOING TO RESUME CONTROL OF HONG KONG AND THERE WERE SIGNS EVERYWHERE ANNOUNCING THIS. MOTHER AND I HAD INTERESTING DISCUSSIONS ABOUT THIS EVENT AND IT SEEMED AS IF SHE WERE HER USUAL SELF. SHE WAS NOT REPEATING HERSELF AND SEEMED "NORMAL".

ONE DAY WE DECIDED TO GO TO A MUSEUM WE HAD NOT VISITED BEFORE. WE WERE LOOKING AT THE CHINESE PORCELAINS AND SHE SAID, "I WONDER WHATEVER HAPPENED TO COUSIN LULA BELLE AND ALL HER

CHINESE PORCELAINS?" I KNEW MY GRANDFATHER HAD IMPORTED PORCELAIN VASES FROM THE ORIENT. HE HAD DIED WHEN MOTHER WAS 18 SO I NEVER HEARD MUCH ABOUT THE BUSINESS. TO MY KNOWLEDGE HE HAD NO BROTHERS OR SISTERS, AND MOTHER HAD NO AUNTS OR UNCLES FROM HER FATHER'S SIDE. SUDDENLY SHE IS ASKING ABOUT A COUSIN I NEVER HEARD OF.

I ASKED WHO COUSIN LULA BELLE WAS AND SHE SAID"OH, YOU KNOW. MY FATHER HAD 2 BROTHERS AND 2 SISTERS AND THEY ALL HAD ONE CHILD, ALL OF WHOM WERE GIRLS." LULA BELLE, ACCORDING TO MOTHER, WAS HER FIRST COUSIN. SHE WENT ON TO TELL ME THAT LULA BELLE HAD LIVED IN CHINA WITH HER PARENTS WHEN THEY WERE IMPORTING PORCELAINS INTO THE STATES, AND THAT SHE HAD WONDERFUL CHINESE VASES AND MANY OF THEM. I WAS TOTALLY FLABBERGASTED. I WAS 52 YEARS OLD AT THE TIME, AND THIS WAS THE FIRST TIME I HAD HEARD ABOUT THESE RELATIVES. INSTEAD OF MY BELIEVING MOTHER, I WAS CONCERNED THAT SHE WAS MAKING THIS STORY UP. I HAD NO WAY OF CHECKING IT OUT AT THAT TIME. NOR HAVE I REALLY TRIED TO SINCE.

BY THE TIME WE GOT BACK TO CLEVELAND I WAS VERY CONCERNED. I CALLED OUR INTERNIST SEEKING HELP. HE SUGGESTED THAT THE NEXT TIME MOTHER WAS IN HE WOULD SCHEDULE A HEARING TEST FOR HER, EVEN THOUGH NEITHER OF US THOUGHT HER HEARING WAS THE PROBLEM. AT LEAST THE TEST WOULD ELIMINATE THAT POSSIBILITY. SHE WILLINGLY HAD THE HEARING TEST, AND HER HEARING WAS FINE. AFTER THAT THE DOCTOR SUGGESTED TO HER THAT SHE HAVE A MEMORY TEST. HE TOLD HER IT WOULD BE A GOOD WAY TO PROVE ME WRONG, WHICH WAS THE PERFECT WAY TO APPROACH MY MOTHER. SHE TOOK THE INFORMATION BUT NEVER MADE THE APPOINTMENT FOR THE MEMORY TEST.

SHE DID TELL ME WHAT THE DOCTOR SAID AND THAT SHE HAD THE INFORMATION. AFTER A COUPLE OF WEEKS WHEN SHE DID NOT MENTION AN APPOINTMENT, I ASKED HER IF SHE HAD MADE ONE. SHE HAD NOT, AND WEEKS WENT BY WITHOUT HER DOING SO. I KEPT ASKING HER ABOUT IT. FINALLY I CALLED THE DOCTOR AND GOT THE INFORMATION MYSELF AND MADE AN APPOINTMENT FOR MOTHER. TAKING SOME CONTROL OF HER LIFE WAS VERY UNCOMFORTABLE FOR ME, BUT I HAD TO KNOW WHAT WAS GOING ON, AND IF THERE WERE ANYTHING THAT COULD BE DONE TO IMPROVE THE SITUATION AND HELP HER.

ONCE WE HAD GOTTEN HOME FROM THE OVERSEAS TRIP, MOTHER WAS SOMEWHAT BETTER. SHE WAS NOT AS REPETITIVE AND SHE SEEMED TO BE FUNCTIONING IN HER NORMAL DAY- TO -DAY ROUTINE. SHE WAS STILL LIVING ALONE AND STILL DRIVING. IT WAS EASY FOR ME AT THE TIME TO RATIONALIZE THAT THE MEMORY LOSS WAS DUE TO NEW SITUATIONS AND THAT IN HER EVERYDAY ENVIRONMENT SHE WOULD BE FINE.

I CAN STILL SEE HER LOOK WHEN I TOLD HER I HAD MADE AN APPOINTMENT FOR HER MEMORY TEST. SHE WAS HORRIFIED AND ANGRY. I WONDERED IF WHAT I WAS DOING WAS THE RIGHT THING TO DO. HOWEVER, I DID NOT CANCEL THE APPOINTMENT AND I TOLD HER TO MARK HER CALENDAR.

WHEN THE DAY OF HER MEMORY TEST APPOINTMENT ARRIVED I PICKED HER UP. BOTH OF US, I THINK, WERE NERVOUS ABOUT WHAT WAS IN STORE FOR HER AND FOR US. IT'S ONE THING TO THINK SOMETHING IS WRONG. THE FINALITY OF KNOWING IS VERY DIFFERENT FROM THE ANTICIPATION. I THINK THAT IS PART OF THE REASON SO MANY SPOUSES AND FAMILY MEMBERS GO INTO DENIAL WHEN THEY SEE A LOVED ONE LOSING MEMORY. THE MEMORY LOSS OF A FAMILY MEMBER OR FRIEND AFFECTS EVERYONE THAT HAS CONTACT WITH THE PERSON WITH MEMORY LOSS AND CHANGES LIVES FOREVER.

WE ARE LUCKY IN CLEVELAND TO HAVE ONE OF 30 RESEARCH CENTERS IN THE COUNTRY THAT CAN TEST FOR SEVERE MEMORY LOSS. THIS CENTER IS IN THE SAME BUILDING AS THE ALZHEIMER'S ASSOCIATION CLEVELAND AREA CHAPTER. AT THE TIME MOTHER AND I FIRST WENT TO THE RESEARCH CENTER THERE WAS LITTLE IF ANY COORDINATION BETWEEN THE RESEARCH CENTER AND THE ALZHEIMER'S ASSOCIATION. THE RESEARCH CENTER DID NOT LIKE USING THE WORD "ALZHEIMER'S" AND INSTEAD USED "SEVERE MEMORY LOSS". HOWEVER, THE RESEARCH CENTER DOCTORS WERE ABLE TO PRESCRIBE MEDICINES THAT WERE IN FDA TESTING STAGES, AND THIS, IN MY MIND, MADE GOING THERE WORTHWHILE.

WE MET WITH DR PETER WHITEHOUSE ON FEBUARY 25, 1997. DR. WHITEHOUSE IS IN CHARGE OF RESEARCH. HE DID A SHORT MEMORY TEST WITH MOTHER. SHE ACTUALLY DID FAIRLY WELL WITH IT, WHICH BOOSTED HER SPIRITS AND MADE ME WONDER – AGAIN - IF I WERE DOING THE RIGHT THING. DR. WHITEHOUSE SUGGESTED MOTHER GO THROUGH A SERIES OF EXTENSIVE TESTS WITH THE STAFF. SHE DID SO ON MARCH 5TH AND AGAIN

ON MARCH 21ST. THIS PROCESS TOOK OVER TWO HOURS BOTH DAYS. I WAS EXHAUSTED JUST SITTING IN THE WAITING ROOM; I CAN ONLY IMAGINE HOW DIFFICULT THE TESTING WAS FOR MOTHER.

AT THIS POINT I NEED TO DIGRESS SOME TO EXPLAIN A LITTLE ABOUT MY MOTHER, HER INTELLIGENCE AND HER PERSONALITY. SHE WAS AN ONLY CHILD, AND AS SHE AGED, SHE MENTIONED THIS POINT A LOT TO EXPLAIN WHY SHE WAS NOT BEING VERY SOCIAL. SHE WOULD SAY SHE WAS VERY CONTENT BEING BY HERSELF IN HER LOVELY APARTMENT WITH HER BOOKS. UP TO A POINT THIS WAS PROBABLY TRUE. BUT PRIOR TO MY SISTER'S DEATH ALMOST TWO YEARS EARLIER, MOTHER HADAN ACTIVE SOCIAL LIFE. AFTER MY SISTER DIED FROM LUNG CANCER, I AM SURE MOTHER HAD SOME DEPRESSION, AND I EXPECT THE DEPRESSION CONTINUED THROUGHOUT THE ENTIRE PROCESS OF HER ALZHEIMER'S. BUT I AM GETTING AHEAD OF MYSELF.

MOTHER WAS EXTREMELY INTELLIGENT. SHE HAD BEEN IN A SPECIAL EDUCATION CLASS THROUGHOUT MOST OF HER SCHOOLING BECAUSE OF HER HIGH IQ. SHE HAD INTENDED TO GO ON TO COLLEGE AFTER GRADUATION FROM HIGH SCHOOL, BUT HER FATHER SUDDENLY DIED OF A HEART ATTACK, AND THERE WAS NO MONEY FOR COLLEGE. THIS WAS IN 1936. VERY FEW WOMEN WENT TO COLLEGE IN THOSE YEARS. INSTEAD OF ATTENDING COLLEGE, SHE BECAME AN EXECUTIVE SECRETARY. SHE TOOK CARE OF HERSELF AND HER MOTHER WHILE SHE WAS WORKING. THEN IN 1941 SHE MET MY FATHER AND THEY MARRIED IN 1942. HER WORKING DAYS WERE OVER.

OVER THE YEARS MOTHER DID SOME CHARITY WORK, BUT THAT WAS BASICALLY MY FATHER'S PASSION, NOT HERS. HER JOB WAS TO TAKE CARE OF THE HOUSE, ME AND MY SISTER. SHE SEEMED PERFECTLY CONTENT TO DO THAT. I REMEMBER WHEN I WAS IN HIGH SCHOOL I TRIED TO ENCOURAGE HER TO DO SOMETHING THAT I THOUGHT WOULD BE MORE PRODUCTIVE. SHE HAD SUCH A GOOD BRAIN THEN, AND I THOUGHT IT WAS NOT BEING USED TO ITS FULLEST. IT'S BECAUSE OF THAT GOOD BRAIN THAT THIS PROCESS OF MEMORY LOSS WAS EVEN MORE DIFFICULT FOR HER AND FOR ME.

THE TEST RESULTS SHOWED DEFINITE MEMORY LOSS, AND DR. WHITEHOUSE SET HER UP ON A REGULAR SCHEDULE TO SEE HIM SO THAT HE COULD MONITOR THE PROGRESSION OF THE MEMORY LOSS. HE

EXPLAINED TO US THAT THERE IS NO NORMAL PATTERN WHEN IT COMES TO MEMORY LOSS. EACH PERSON IS DIFFERENT. OFTEN A PERSON WILL REACH A PLATEAU AND STAY THERE FOR AWHILE; OTHER TIMES THERE IS A STEADY DOWNHILL LOSS OF MEMORY. I THINK THIS UNCERTAINTY ADDED TO THE FRUSTRATION. I HAD GONE THROUGH THE SIX MONTHS OF MY SISTER'S LUNG CANCER AND KNEW PRETTY MUCH WHAT TO EXPECT ALONG THE WAY. I HAD NO IDEA WHAT TO EXPECT WITH ALZHEIMER'S AND HAD SOME MOMENTS OF SHEER PANIC.

IN AN EFFORT TO STOP THE PANIC STAGE, I STARTED SOME RESEARCH. I CALLED THE ALZHEIMER'S ASSOCIATION AND SIGNED UP FOR A SUPPORT GROUP. I NEEDED TO KNOW MORE, A LOT MORE, IN ORDER TO DEAL WITH WHAT WAS AHEAD FOR US. MY SENSE OF REALITY WAS DISAPPEARING DAILY, AND I NEEDED SOMEONE/SOMETHING TO HELP GET ME GROUNDED. I NEEDED TO HELP MYSELF IN ORDER TO HELP MY MOTHER.

CHAPTER TWO
DISCOVERING I HAVE NO MAP

YOU LEARN TO LIVE IN THE WORLD OF THE ALZHEIMER'S PATIENT RATHER THAN TRYING TO FORCE HER/HIM TO LIVE IN YOURS.

AT THIS POINT MOTHER WAS REALLY FUNCTIONING. IF YOU DID NOT SPEND A LOT OF TIME WITH HER, YOU WOULD NOT DETECT ANY PROBLEMS. THE MAIN SYMPTOM THAT ANYTHING WAS WRONG WAS HER CONSTANT REPETITIVENESS. WE OFTEN HAD THE SAME CONVERSATION, OVER AND OVER AGAIN. SHE WAS STILL ABLE TO DRIVE, GO OUT WITH HER FRIENDS, GO TO HER WEEKLY CARD GAME AND ENJOY HER REGULAR ACTIVITIES. HER APARTMENT WAS NEAT; SHE WAS WELL GROOMED, AND MY FRIENDS ALL THOUGHT I WAS OVER REACTING.EVEN I WAS WONDERING IF I WAS BEING OVERLY SENSITIVE, EVEN WITH THE TEST RESULTS SHOWING THE MEMORY LOSS. WE OFTEN HAD DINNER WITH MY BEST FRIEND KAREN, HER HUSBAND AND HER FATHER. KAREN WOULD TELL ME THAT ALWAYS AFTER WE LEFT BEING WITH THEM HER FATHER WOULD COMMENT THAT, "NOTHING IS WRONG WITH RUTH. WHY DOES LYN THINK THERE IS?" WHAT HE COULD NOT KNOW WAS THAT MUCH OF WHAT MY MOTHER WAS SAYING IN CONVERSATION WAS NOT TRUE. IT ALWAYS SOUNDED RIGHT, BUT IT WAS OFTEN SOMETHING THAT HAD HAPPENED YEARS AGO THAT MOTHER MADE SOUND AS IF IT HAD HAPPENED YESTERDAY. SOMETIMES IT HAD NOT HAPPENED AT ALL.YET SOMEHOW MOTHER STILL HAD THE ABILITY TO MAKE SENSE IN A CONVERSATION WITH OTHERS. OFTEN I NOTICED THAT SHE USED A WRONG WORD FOR WHAT SHE WAS TRYING TO SAY, SUCH AS APPLE WHEN SHE MEANT ORANGE, BUT IT STILL MADE SENSE.

EARLY ON I TOLD THE MANAGER IN HER CONDO THAT MOTHER HAD BEEN DIAGNOSED WITH ALZHEIMER'S. I ASKED HIM TO TELL THE STAFF AND TO KEEP AN EXTRA EYE OUT FOR HER. HE WAS AMAZED THAT I WAS TELLING HIM THIS, NOT BECAUSE HE WAS UNAWARE OF HER HAVING SOME MEMORY PROBLEMS BUT BECAUSE HE SAID USUALLY HE HAD TO TELL THE FAMILY, NOT THE OTHER WAY AROUND. HE TOLD ME HOW MOTHER WOULD OFTEN STOP IN THE OFFICE AND ASK SOMETHING THAT SHE HAD ASKED JUST THE DAY BEFORE, AND THAT HE HAD BEEN THINKING ABOUT CALLING ME TO LET ME KNOW HIS SUSPICIONS ABOUT HER MEMORY.

THEN SLOWLY OTHER THINGS STARTED HAPPENING.

SHE MISSED SOME APPPOINTMENTS. SHE WAS EITHER EARLY OR LATE FOR OTHERS. ONCE SHE WAS SUPPOSED TO BE AT MY HOUSE FOR DINNER AND WAS NOT THERE ON TIME. "ON TIME" IN OUR FAMILY ALWAYS MEANT TEN MINUTES EARLY. AFTER THIRTY MINUTES I STARTED TO WORRY. AFTER ANOTHER TEN MINUTES I STARTED TO PANIC. I CALLED HER APARTMENT. I CALLED THE GATEHOUSE AT HER CONDO TO SEE IF THE GUARD COULD CHECK ON HER OR SEE IF HER CAR WAS IN THE GARAGE. SHE WAS NOT HOME AND THE CAR WAS GONE. FINALLY SHE SHOWED UP. SHE SAID SHE HAD GONE TO THE WRONG HOUSE AND HAD BEEN RINGING THE DOORBELL FOR SEVERAL MINUTES UNTIL SHE REALIZED SHE WAS AT THE WRONG PLACE. MY REACTION WAS RELIEF AND ANGER AT HER FOR PUTTING ME THROUGH SUCH WORRY. THAT REACTION OF BOTH RELIEF AND ANGER WAS WHAT I LEARNED TO LIVE WITH FOR THE NEXT SEVERAL MONTHS. I KNEW THE ANGER WAS NOT FAIRLY DIRECTED AT HER. WHAT WAS HAPPENING WAS BEYOND HER CONTROL. THAT DOES NOT MEAN THAT I DID NOT REGULARLY FEEL THE ANGER OR IMPATIENCE ABOUT HER SITUATION AND TOWARDS HER, FAIRLY OR NOT.

EARLY IN THIS JOURNEY WE WENT TO WICHITA, KANSAS TO VISIT SOME FRIENDS AND SEE AN EXHIBIT FROM RUSSIA. WE HAD TRAVELED IN RUSSIA TOGETHER A FEW MONTHS AFTER MY SISTER HAD DIED, AND I THOUGHT GOING ON THIS TRIP TO WICHITA WOULD BE SOMETHING FUN FOR US TO DO TOGETHER. I GAVE MOTHER VERY THOROUGH INSTRUCTIONS ON WHERE TO MEET ME AFTER I PARKED THE CAR. IN THE PAST I WOULD NOT HAVE HAD TO DO THIS. WHEN I GOT TO THE CHECK-IN COUNTER WHERE SHE WAS SUPPOSED TO MEET ME, SHE WAS NOT THERE. AGAIN, THIS WAS VERY EARLY ON WITH HER MEMORY LOSS. SHE WAS STILL FUNCTIONING ON SO MANY LEVELS. IT HAD NOT BEEN A WORRY TO DROP HER OFF AT THE AIRPORT WHERE SHE HAD BEEN SO MANY TIMES BEFORE. HOWEVER, THE REST OF THE TRIP I KEPT WATCH OVER HER MORE CAREFULLY. WHAT I LEARNED IS THAT ONE GOOD MOMENT DOES NOT MEAN TEN GOOD MOMENTS AND THAT I COULD NOT KNOW AHEAD OF TIME WHEN THE GOOD MOMENTS WOULD HAPPEN OR WHEN MOTHER'S MEMORY WOULD NOT BE THERE.

I FOUND MOTHER JUST WANDERING AROUND THE AREA. SHE WAS UNCONCERNED. I WAS FRANTIC. THIS BECAME THE PATTERN OF OUR REACTIONS FOR THE NEXT SEVERAL YEARS.

ONE DAY ONE OF MY NEIGHBORS CALLED ME TO SAY HE HAD SEEN MY MOTHER IN HER CAR. SHE HAD PULLED OVER TO THE SIDE OF THE ROAD AND WAS JUST SITTING, AS IF SHE WERE LOST. SHE WAS PARKED NEAR OUR OLD HOUSE, WHICH WAS THE NEIGHBORHOOD I NOW LIVED IN. HE HAD DECIDED NOT TO STOP AND ASK HER IF SHE NEEDED ANY HELP BECAUSE SHE DID NOT KNOW HIM AND MIGHT HAVE BEEN AFRAID. INSTEAD HE CAME HOME AND CALLED ME. THIS WAS THE FIRST OF MANY TIMES THAT SHE SEEMED LOST IN THE NEIGHBORHOOD. SHE AND DAD HAD MOVED INTO THE CONDO TWENTY SOME YEARS EARLIER BUT THEY HAD LIVED IN THAT HOUSE AND THIS NEIGHBORHOOD FOR OVER THIRTY YEARS. HERE WAS SOME LONG TERM MEMORY NOT WORKING, WHICH WAS REALLY SCARY.

WHETHER SHE WOULD HAVE BEEN AFRAID OR NOT OF MY NEIGHBOR I CANNOT EVER KNOW. I SUSPECT SHE WOULD NOT HAVE BEEN AFRAID FOR ONE DAY I GOT A CALL FROM HER TO SAY THAT HER CAR WOULD NOT START. SHE WAS AT A SHOPPING MALL NEAR HER APARTMENT AND SHE ASKED WHAT SHE SHOULD DO. I SUGGESTED CALLING AAA OR ONSTAR (CADILLAC) TO COME AND JUMP THE BATTERY. THIS WAS STILL EARLY ON IN THE DISEASE. WHAT SHE DID, INSTEAD, WAS ASK A TOTAL STRANGER TO DRIVE HER HOME. SHE CALLED ME WHEN SHE GOT HOME. I WAS HORRIFIED; MOTHER WOULD NEVER HAVE DONE THIS IN THE PAST. SHE WAS SUCH A SNOB THAT SHE WOULD NEVER EVEN TALK TO STRANGERS, LET ALONE GET IN A CAR WITH ONE.

SHE COULD NOT UNDERSTAND WHY I WAS SO UPSET.

LATER I PICKED HER UP AND WE WENT TO THE CAR TOGETHER AND WAITED FOR AAA TO COME AND JUMP THE BATTERY. WHEN THIS HAPPENED SHE COULD NOT FIND THE APARTMENT KEYS. I HAD ALL SORTS OF WORRIES ABOUT THIS STRANGER HAVING THE KEYS. MY ONLY CONSOLATION WAS THAT MOTHER LIVED IN A GATED COMMUNITY. LATER, OF COURSE, WE FOUND THE KEYS. THIS WAS THE BEGINNING OF HER CONSTANTLY MISPLACING THINGS.

DURING THIS PERIOD I HAD BEEN TELLING ONE OF MY FRIENDS SOME OF WHAT WAS GOING ON. SHE AND I WERE HAVING A DAY OF FUN. IT WAS A BEAUTIFUL SPRING DAY WITH THE SUN SHINING AND FLOWERS BLOOMING. SUDDENLY MY FRIEND SAID TO ME THAT SHE WAS SURE I WAS EXAGGERATING, THAT THERE WAS NO WAY MY MOTHER COULD BE DOING

THE THINGS I SAID. THAT REALLY SHOOK ME UP. THE SUNSHINE OF THE DAY SUDDENLY HAD GREY CLOUDS. I WAS SURE I WAS NOT EXAGGERATING OR MAKING THINGS UP. I WONDERED WHY MY FRIEND DID NOT BELIEVE ME. WHY, I WONDERED, IS MY FRIEND IN DENIAL ABOUT MY MOTHER?

FORTUNATELY DURING THIS TIME I HAD STARTED THE SUPPORT GROUP WITH THE ALZHEIMER'S ASSOCIATION. THE GROUP WAS SET UP IN TWO FORTY-FIVE MINUTE SESSIONS. THE FIRST FORTY-FIVE MINUTES WAS WITH THE ENTIRE FAMILY UNIT, THE CAREGIVERS AND THE PERSONS WITH ALZHEIMER'S. THE SECOND HALF WE BROKE UP INTO THREE GROUPS: PERSONS WITH ALZHEIMER'S, THEIR SPOUSES AND THEIR CHILDREN OR OTHER CAREGIVERS. IT WAS COMFORTING TO TALK OPENLY WITH OTHER CHILDREN GOING THROUGH THE SAME EMOTIONS AND SITUATIONS AND HAVING THE SAME THOUGHTS AND REACTIONS AS I WAS.

ONE THING I NOTICED WAS HOW MUCH DENIAL COMES WITH THIS DISEASE. IF THERE WERE MORE THAN ONE CHILD IN THE FAMILY, THE SIBLINGS OFTEN DID NOT AGREE ON THE SERIOUSNESS OF THE PROBLEM OR ON HOW TO HANDLE IT. OFTEN ONE OF THEM THOUGHT THE PARENT WAS OK. IT WAS ALSO OBVIOUS THAT MANY SPOUSES OF THE PERSONS WITH ALZHEIMER'S MANAGE TO HIDE THE DEGREE OF MEMORY LOSS FROM THEIR CHILDREN. THE SPOUSE WLL START TO DO MORE AND MORE FOR THE PERSON WITH ALZHEIMER'S AND IN THIS WAY "COVERS UP" THE FACT THAT SOMETHING IS "WRONG" WITH THE SPOUSE – COVERING IT UP TO HER/HIMSELF AND TO THE CHILDREN. IF THE CHILDREN DO NOT SEE THE PARENTS REGULARLY, AS IS OFTEN THE CASE IN TODAY'S WORLD OF CHILDREN LIVING IN DIFFERENT CITIES FROM THEIR PARENTS, THIS COVER UP CAN GO ON FOR MANY MONTHS. I AM NOT SURE IT IS ALWAYS INTENTIONAL. I DO KNOW IT IS HARMFUL. I SUSPECT IT HAPPENS ALMOST NATURALLY, WITHOUT THE SPOUSE REALIZING IT. WHEN FAMILY MEMBERS HAVE AN ILLNESS LIKE CANCER THERE IS GRIEF AND THEN EVERYONE DOES WHATEVER NECESSARY TO HELP THE ILL PERSON SURVIVE/GET BETTER/ BEAT THE ILLNESS. THIS DOES NOT HAPPEN WITH ALZHEIMER'S. THERE IS NO SUCH THING AS "BEATING" THIS DISEASE. I SUSPECT IT CONTRIBUTES TO THE DENIAL FACTOR.

THIS DISEASE IS SOMETHING THAT FAMILIES MUST LEARN TO GO THROUGH TOGETHER. IT IS SO EMOTIONAL AND EVEN PHYSICALLY DRAINING, ESPECIALLY ON THE DAY- TO- DAY CAREGIVER, THAT WITHOUT FAMILY SUPPORT, THE CAREGIVER IS LIKELY TO GET RUN DOWN OR EVEN SICK.

THEN THE CHILDREN HAVE TWO PARENTS TO WORRY ABOUT.

THERE WERE SEVERAL THINGS THAT BECAME EVIDENT WHILE SITTING
THROUGH THE SUPPORT GROUP SESSIONS. THE FIRST WAS OF A PRACTICAL
NATURE. MOST OF THE FAMILIES WERE WORRIED ABOUT THE FINANCIAL
DRAIN OF THIS DISEASE. IN SOME CASES A FAMILY MEMBER WAS GOING
TO HAVE TO QUIT A JOB IN ORDER TO CARE FOR A PARENT. IN OTHER
CASES PARENTS' HOUSES WERE HAVING TO BE SOLD IN ORDER TO AFFORD
HAVING A PARENT IN AN ASSISTED LIVING FACILITY OR A NURSING HOME.
I ALWAYS WALKED OUT OF THESE MEETINGS FEELING THANKFUL THAT
MONEY WAS NOT ONE OF THE MANY THINGS I WAS WORRYING ABOUT
AND HAVING A REAL APPRECIATION OF HOW DIFFICULT THE MONEY
WORRY MUST BE. IT'S ONE OF THE REASONS FOR WRITING THIS BOOK.
I AM HOPING TO INFORM FAMILIES OF WHAT COULD BE IN STORE FOR
THEM SO THAT THERE IS EARLY PLANNING. IN THE NEXT X NUMBER OF
YEARS, MORE AND MORE FAMILIES WILL HAVE TO DEAL WITH A LOVED
ONE BEING DIAGNOSED WITH THIS DISEASE. WE SAVE FOR COLLEGE FOR
OUR CHILDREN; WE SAVE FOR OUR RETIREMENT. WE DO NOT SAVE FOR THE
LIKELIHOOD OF OUR PARENTS NEEDING CARE FOR ALZHEIMER'S, OR FOR
THAT MATTER, ANY OTHER DISEASES. IN THE CASE OF ALZHEIMER'S, MOST
OF US WILL NOT HAVE ANY INSURANCE MONEY THAT WILL HELP WITH THE
BURDEN.

ANOTHER THING THAT WAS OBVIOUS TO ME FROM ATTENDING THE
SUPPORT GROUP MEETINGS WAS HOW UNREALISTIC MOST OF THE FAMILIES
WERE ABOUT THIS DISEASE. MANY WERE STILL IN DENIAL. MOST DID NOT
WANT TO DEAL WITH IT ON ANY LEVEL. SIBLINGS OFTEN DISAGREE ON
WHAT TO DO. IN TURN THE CHILDREN, WHO ARE ADULTS IN THEIR OWN
RIGHT, DISAGREE WITH THE PARENT WHO WAS THE CAREGIVER. MANY
OF THE CHILDREN LIVED OUT OF TOWN. THAT COMPLICATED THE ISSUES.
DECISIONS DID NOT GET MADE. OFTEN IF ANY DECISIONS WERE MADE,
THE INDIVIDUAL WITH ALZHEIMER'S WAS NOT INVOLVED IN THE DECISION
PROCESS BECAUSE THEY WERE NO LONGER ABLE TO BE INVOLVED.

THIS WAS SOMETHING I DID NOT WANT TO BE THE CASE WITH MY MOTHER.
SHE HAD ALWAYS BEEN A REALIST AND I THOUGHT IT IMPORTANT TO HOLD
ONTO THAT PART OF HER PERSONALITY. I STARTED FRANKLY TALKING WITH
HER ABOUT HER HAVING ALZHEMIER'S AS SOON AS WE KNEW THERE WAS
A CONFIRMED DIAGNOSIS; I WANTED HER TO BE ABLE TO TELL ME WHAT
SHE WANTED AND WHAT SHE DID NOT WANT. THIS DID NOT AND WOULD
NOT MEAN THAT I COULD ALWAYS DO WHAT SHE HAD REQUESTED. OFTEN I

HAD TO MAKE THE BEST OF CHOICES IN ORDER TO KEEP HER SAFE INSTEAD OF HAPPY. I LEARNED THAT THERE ARE NOT ANY "RIGHT" DECISIONS. WATCHING A LOVED ONE PROGRESS INTO THE DEPTHS OF ALZHEIMER'S IS AWFUL. KNOWING THAT NO MATTER WHAT DECISION YOU MAKE ALONG THE WAY IS LIKELY NOT TO MAKE IT EASIER, AND CERTAINLY NOT MAKE IT GO AWAY, IS ALSO DEVASTATING.

I WOULD 100% RECOMMEND SUPPORT GROUPS. THEY ARE INFORMATIVE ON SO MANY LEVELS. YOU LEARN ABOUT THE PHYSICAL PROBLEMS, THE MENTAL PROBLEMS AND THE PSYCHOLOGICAL PROBLEMS. YOU LEARN THAT YOU ARE NOT ALONE IN EXPERIENCING THE EMOTIONS OF THIS DISEASE. YOU SOMETIMES LEARN THINGS YOU CAN DO TO MAKE THE PROCESS EASIER. THERE ARE THINGS THAT CAN IMPROVE THE MEMORY SHORT TERM. I KNOW THERE IS A GREAT DEAL OF RESISTANCE FOR SOME TO GO TO THE SUPPORT GROUPS. I COULD NOT HAVE GOTTEN THROUGH THE PROCESS WITHOUT THE GROUPS I ATTENDED. MY ADVICE WOULD BE TO TRY IT AND MAKE YOUR OWN DECISION.

MY MOTHER WAS ON THE MEDICATION ARICEPT FOR A TIME. I THINK IT HELPED SLOW DOWN THE PROGRESSION OF THE DISEASE – FOR A WHILE. IT TOOK SEVERAL WEEKS BEFORE THE RIGHT DOSAGE WAS DECIDED UPON. THE MEDICINE IS RELATIVELY EXPENSIVE, BUT WORTH IT IF IT "BUYS" YOU AND YOUR FAMILY SOME GOOD TIMES WITH YOUR LOVED ONE. MOTHER AND I WERE SEEING DR. WHITEHOUSE FOR HER REGULAR CHECK UP AND HE ASKED HER HOW SHE WAS DOING ON THE ARICEPT. SHE SAID SHE WAS NO LONGER TAKING IT. I NEVER DID FIND OUT IF THIS WAS TRUE OR NOT. I HAD GOTTEN THE MEDICINE FOR HER, BUT THERE WAS NO WAY I COULD REALLY CHECK ON WHAT SHE WAS TAKING AT THIS POINT IN THE JOURNEY. AFTER AWHILE BOTH THE DOCTOR AND I DECIDED THAT WE WOULD NOT HAVE HER TAKE THE ARICEPT AS SHE WAS SO RESISTENT TO DOING SO.

THERE ARE THINGS, BESIDES MEDICINES, THAT YOU CAN DO TO HELP SOMEONE WITH ALZHEIMER'S FUNCTION BETTER – SUCH AS STICKY NOTES ALL OVER THE HOUSE, PUTTING CLOTHING OUTFITS TOGETHER FOR YOUR LOVED ONE, PUTTING LARGE NOTES ON THE REFRIGERATOR THAT THE KITCHEN IS CLOSED ONCE DINNER HAS BEEN EATEN SO THAT YOUR LOVED ONE DOES NOT TRY TO PREPARE ANOTHER MEAL. SOMEONE WITH ALZHEIMER'S WILL OFTEN FORGET THEY HAVE EATEN, OR FORGET TO EAT. THE NATIONAL ALZHEIMER'S ASSOCIATION IN CHICAGO HAS AN EXCELLENT BROCHURE AS PART OF THEIR ACTION SERIES ENTITLED

"STEPS TO ENHANCING YOUR HOME, MODIFYING THE ENVIRONMENT", THAT I WOULD HIGHLY RECOMMEND AS A GUIDE.

YOU LEARN THAT THINGS YOU THOUGHT MATTERED DON'T. YOU LEARN TO LIVE IN THE WORLD OF THE PERSON WITH ALZHEIMER'S RATHER THAN TRYING TO FORCE HER/HIM TO LIVE IN YOURS. THIS WAS THE MOST IMPORTANT THING I LEARNED IN ONE OF THE SUPPORT GROUP SESSIONS. IT HELPED ME REPEATEDLY AS I WAS GOING THROUGH THIS JOURNEY WITH MY MOTHER.

EVERYTHING YOU KNOW UP UNTIL YOU ARE CARING FOR SOMEONE WITH ALZHEIMER'S, ESPECIALLY A PARENT, DOES NOT APPLY. THE ROAD MAPS ARE MISSING LOCATIONS AND PLACES THAT YOU THINK SHOULD BE THERE. HOW YOU REACTED IN THE PAST TO SOMETHING NO LONGER IS VALID. THERE IS NO LOGIC TO THIS DISEASE. FRUSTRATION IS CONSTANT. DECISION MAKING SEEMS IMPOSSIBLE. THE DISEASE, HOWEVER, DOES NOT WAIT FOR YOU TO ACCEPT IT OR BE COMFORTABLE ABOUT IT. THE ROAD JUST CONTINUES TO TWIST AND CURVE.

ONE OF MY FRIENDS TAKES IMAGINARY TRIPS WITH HER FATHER WHO HAS ALZHEIMER'S. THEY BOTH SHUT THEIR EYES, AND SHE TALKS ABOUT THEIR GOING TO THE BEACH OR TO NEW YORK CITY. HER FATHER TALKS ABOUT HIS MEMORIES OF THOSE PLACES AND IMAGINES THE SMELL OF THE OCEAN. IT IS A HAPPY TIME FOR BOTH OF THEM, AND A CALM TIME FOR HIM.

A COUSIN OF MINE TOLD ME HOW SHE USED TO GO TO VISIT HER MOM IN A NURSING HOME. HER MOTHER HAD ALZHEIMER'S AND WAS ALWAYS PUTTING ON THE "WRONG" BLOUSE WITH THE "WRONG" SKIRT. FOR MONTHS SHE WOULD GO TO SEE HER MOM AND ASK HER WHY SHE HAD ON THOSE CLOTHES TOGETHER. SOMETIMES THEY WERE NOT EVEN HER MOTHER'S CLOTHES. WHAT MY COUSIN COULD NOT ACCEPT WAS THAT HER MOTHER COULD NOT COORDINATE HER CLOTHES ANYMORE, AND THAT HER MOTHER DID NOT CARE. HER MOTHER WAS PERFECTLY HAPPY WITH WHATEVER SHE HAD ON. ONCE MY COUSIN RECOGNIZED THIS, SHE STOPPED ASKING HER MOTHER ABOUT THE CLOTHES AND THEY HAD MUCH MORE PEACEFUL TIMES TOGETHER.

A VOLUNTEER AT THE ALZHEIMER'S ASSOCIATION AT ONE OF THE SUPPORT GROUP MEETINGS TOLD THE STORY OF HER FATHER WHO LIVED WITH HER.

SHE WAS HAVING A DINNER PARTY. ALL OF HER FRIENDS KNEW HER DAD AND KNEW HE HAD ALZHEIMER'S. BEFORE HER FRIENDS ARRIVED FOR DINNER, SHE ASKED HER FATHER TO CHANGE HIS CLOTHES. HE CAME BACK WITH HIS PAJAMA BOTTOM ON AND A REGULAR SHIRT. IN THE PAST SHE WOULD HAVE FUSSED AND MADE HIM CHANGE. SHE WOULD HAVE BEEN EMBARRASSED. INSTEAD SHE JUST LET HIM BE. SHE KNEW HER FRIENDS WOULD NOT CARE, AND SHE LEARNED NOT TO CARE EITHER. THIS IS A GIANT LEAP IN THE ACCEPTANCE PROCESS.

AND IT IS A VERY HARD LEAP FOR MOST OF US TO MAKE.

CHAPTER THREE
THE ROAD NOT TAKEN

I HAD BEEN ON A GARDEN WALK AND ONE OF THE GARDENS WAS AT A NURSING HOME THAT HAPPENED TO HAVE AN ALZHEIMER'S WING. WHILE I WAS THERE I ASKED IF THERE WAS ANYONE AVAILABLE TO SHOW ME THROUGH THE ALZHEIMER'S WING. I HAD NOT BEEN IN ONE BEFORE AND WANTED TO KNOW WHAT IT WOULD BE LIKE, WHAT PERHAPS MY MOTHER WOULD HAVE TO BE IN AT SOME POINT.

A SOCIAL WORKER TOOK ME INTO A LOCKED AND SECURE AREA. THAT WAS MY FIRST TASTE OF THE REALITY OF ALZHEIMER'S – THE NEED TO PREVENT WANDERING PATIENTS. ONE OF THE WOMEN WAS BENT OVER IN HER CHAIR. SHE APPEARED TO BE SLEEPING. WHEN WE WALKED IN THIS WOMAN BECAME SOMEWHAT LIVELY. THE STAFF MEMBER SAID HELLO TO THIS WOMAN. THE WOMAN SAID, "DO I KNOW YOU?" THE STAFF MEMBER SAID, "YES, I'M IN CHARGE OF ACTIVITIES AND SOMETIMES I BRING YOU ICE CREAM." THE WOMAN REPLIED, " I DON'T THINK I KNOW YOU, BUT YOU SEEM NICE. I WOULD LIKE TO KNOW YOU." IT BROKE MY HEART TO HEAR THIS, AND I SO DREADED THE LIKELIHOOD THAT SOMEDAY MY MOTHER WOULD NOT KNOW WHO I WAS.

ONCE I GOT HOME FROM THIS WALK, I MADE THE DECISION TO PUT MOTHER'S NAME ON A LIST FOR THE ASSISTED LIVING FACILITY NEAR HER CONDO. I KNEW FROM FRIENDS THAT IT OFTEN TOOK MONTHS BEFORE THERE WAS ANY AVAILABILITY OF AN APARTMENT. MOTHER WAS NOT READY FOR THIS KIND OF MOVE; NEITHER WAS I. HOWEVER, I KNEW THAT I NEEDED TO PLAN FOR THE FUTURE.

VERY RELUCTANTLY, MOTHER WENT WITH ME TO SEE THE FACILITY AND TALK WITH THE DIRECTOR. WE PUT DOWN A SMALL DEPOSIT AND I FILLED OUT ALL OF THE PAPERWORK. MOTHER KNEW A FEW PEOPLE THERE AND THE FACILITY WAS LOVELY SO IT WAS NOT A TERRIBLE EXPERIENCE FOR HER TO BE THERE FOR THE HOUR. WE BOTH KNEW THAT THIS KIND OF MOVE WAS IN THE FUTURE, AND WAS NOT GOING TO HAPPEN IMMEDIATELY, WHICH MADE IT EASIER AND HARDER AT THE SAME TIME.

AFTER SEVEN MONTHS THE DIRECTOR CALLED TO SAY THERE WAS AN APARTMENT AVAILABLE. MOTHER DID NOT QUITE NEED IT YET – AND I WAS NOT READY TO MOVE HER, SO I TURNED IT DOWN. THE KEY IS THAT I

WAS MAKING JUDGEMENTS FOR BOTH OF US. I WAS NOT READY TO ACCEPT HER BEING IN AN ASSISTED LIVING AND THAT PLAYED AS MUCH IN THE DECISION MAKING AS MY THOUGHTS OF HER NEEDING IT. THE PROCEDURE AT THE ASSISTED LIVING WAS THAT ONCE I TURNED DOWN AN APARTMENT, MOTHER WOULD THEN GO TO THE BOTTOM OF THE LIST. IF I CALLED AT ANY TIME TO SAY WE NEEDED THE APARTMENT SOONER RATHER THAN LATER, THEY WOULD MOVE HER NAME TO THE TOP OF THE LIST. EACH FACILITY IS DIFFERENT. FIND ONE THAT WORKS FOR YOU AND YOUR FAMILY.

I HAD CALLS FROM THE DIRECTOR THREE MORE TIMES BEFORE I CALLED HIM TO TELL HIM TO TAKE HER NAME OFF THE LIST. I HAD MADE THE DECISION TO MOVE US TO FLORIDA AND SO SHE WOULD NOT BE MOVING INTO THE CLEVELAND FACILITY. EACH TIME HE CALLED, MOTHER WAS CLOSER TO NEEDING THE FACILITY, BUT I WAS NOT READY. I RELATE ALL OF THIS TO ASSURE YOU THAT THE DECISION OF HAVING A PARENT MOVE INTO AN ASSISTED LIVING FACILITY IS AN EXTREMELY DIFFICULT ONE.

CHAPTER FOUR
MORE CHANGES IN OUR ITINERARY

EVERY FAMILY HAS ITS OWN ROUTINES. I REMEMBER AS A CHILD AND LATER AS AN ADULT ASKING MY FATHER IF HE WAS GOING TO WORK A FULL DAY ON SATURDAYS. HE ALWAYS REPLIED "YES, HALF A DAY IN THE MORNING AND HALFA DAY IN THE AFTERNOON."

SINCE MY FATHER WORKED ON SATURDAYS, MOTHER HAD HER OWN SATURDAY ROUTINE. SHE HAD A HAIR APPOINTMENT IN THE MIDDLE OF THE MORNING AND THEN WOULD MEET HER FRIENDS AT THE COUNTRY CLUB FOR LUNCH AND CARDS. SEVERAL YEARS BEFORE MOTHER'S ALZHEIMER'S WAS OBVIOUS, A FRIEND OF HERS STARTED GETTING CONFUSED WHEN PLAYING WITH THEM. IT TURNED OUT THAT SHE HAD SOME FORM OF MEMORY LOSS. THE WOMEN IN THE CARD GAME TOLD HER SHE COULD NOT PLAY WITH THEM. THEY DID NOT DO IT KINDLY AS I RECALL, AND MOTHER AND I DISCUSSED IT AT THE TIME AS MOTHER THOUGHT THE WOMEN HAD BEEN SOMEWHAT CRUEL IN THEIR HANDLING OF THIS "FRIEND" AND HER MEMORY LOSS.

WHEN I REALIZED MOTHER HAD ALZHEIMER'S, I CALLED HER BEST FRIEND, WHO WAS IN THE CARD GAME, AND TOLD HER THAT I WAS CONCERNED ABOUT MOTHER'S PLAYING. HER FRIEND TOLD ME THAT MOTHER WAS STILL PLAYING JUST FINE. THE WOMEN WERE NOW ALL IN THEIR LATE 70'S AND EARLY 80'S. SOME OF THEM DID NOT HEAR SO WELL; SOME OF THEM DID NOT EVEN SEE VERY WELL. I WAS HOPEFUL THAT THEY WOULD BE MORE KIND TO MY MOTHER THAN THEY HAD BEEN TO THIS OTHER WOMAN YEARS AGO. THERE WAS A MAN IN THE CIRCLE OF MY PARENTS FRIENDS THAT HAD ALZHEIMER'S MANY YEARS AGO. HE COULD NOT GET TO THE CLUB ON HIS OWN TO PLAY CARDS, BUT ONCE HIS WIFE GOT HIM TO THE CARD GAME, HE COULD PLAY AS WELL AS HE EVER HAD. I WAS HOPING THAT THIS WOULD BE THE CASE WITH MOTHER AS WELL. IT IS A MYSTERY AS TO WHY SOMEONE WITH ALZHEIMER'S CAN PLAY CARDS. PERHAPS IT IS THE DIFFERENCE BETWEEN LONG TERM AND SHORT TERM MEMORY OR PERHAPS THERE IS A DIFFERENCE AS TO WHICH PART OF THE BRAIN IS USED FOR CARDS VERSUS OTHER ACTIVITIES.

THE WOMEN PLAYED MOSTLY BRIDGE SO THIS TOOK SOME

CONCENTRATION AS WELL AS MEMORY. FOR A WHILE THE CARD GAME CONTINUED. THEN MOTHER STARTED TELLING ME THE GAME GOT CANCELLED. AT FIRST I WAS NOT SURE IF SHE WERE SAYING THIS BECAUSE SHE WAS AFRAID TO PLAY, OR IF THE GROUP WAS FORCING HER OUT OF THE GAME. IT TURNED OUT TO BE A COMBINATION OF BOTH. THE WOMEN WERE A LITTLE KINDER THAN THEY HAD BEEN TO THE FIRST WOMAN, BUT NOT MUCH. BY THE TIME THE WOMEN TOLD MOTHER THEY WERE NO LONGER PLAYING CARDS, MOTHER WAS PERFECTLY CONTENT, OR SO IT APPEARED, TO STAY IN HER APTARTMENT WITH HER FAMILIAR THINGS, AND NOT DO MUCH SOCIALIZING. I THINK I WAS MORE UPSET ABOUT THIS CHANGE IN HER ROUTINE THAN SHE WAS. IT WAS A CLEAR INDICATION TO ME THAT WE WERE ENTERING A WORLD OF UNCERTAINTY, AND THAT THERE WOULD BE NO TURNING BACK. MOTHER WAS ENTERING A PERIOD OF SOLITUDE, BOTH CHOSEN AND FORCED UPON HER.

ABOUT THIS SAME TIME I TRIED TO GET MOTHER SOME HELP IN HER APARTMENT. SHE DID NOT SEEM ABLE TO PREPARE FOOD FOR HERSELF AND SHE WAS LOSING SOME WEIGHT. MOTHER WAS ONLY 5'1" (HAVING SHRUNK FROM HER 5'3") AND WEIGHED 120 POUNDS. OVER THE NEXT FEW YEARS HER WEIGHT WENT AS LOW AS 105 AND SHE WAS VERY FRAIL. AT THIS POINT HOWEVER, SHE WAS STILL SOMEWHAT VIGOROUS AND I WANTED HER TO STAY THAT WAY. I WAS ABLE TO FIND A WOMAN TO CARE FOR MOTHER THROUGH THE OFFICE AT THE CONDO WHERE MOTHER LIVED. THIS WOMAN HAD BEEN TAKING CARE OF ANOTHER RESIDENT WHO HAD RECENTLY DIED. SO I HIRED THIS WOMAN TO COME TO THE APARTMENT THREE DAYS A WEEK FOR FOUR HOURS A DAY. SHE WOULD PREPARE MOTHER'S LUNCH AND DINNER, AND TAKE HER OUT TO RUN ANY ERRANDS OR TO ANY APPOINTMENTS. MOTHER, PREDICTABLY, HATED IT. SHE HATED HAVING SOMEONE IN THE HOUSE; SHE HATED NOT BEING ABLE TO TAKE CARE OF HERSELF. AT TIMES SHE SEEMED TO HATE ME FOR FORCING THIS WOMAN ON HER.

WHEN THEY WOULD GO GROCERY SHOPPING, THE CAREGIVER WOULD TELL ME LATER THAT MOTHER WOULD PUT SOME ITEMS INTO THE CART SEVERAL TIMES. MOTHER WAS WORKING OFF SEVERAL LISTS. SHE WOULD NOT REMEMBER THAT SHE HAD PUT MILK IN THE CART FROM ONE LIST, AND SO WOULD TAKE MILK FROM A DIFFERENT LIST. THE CAREGIVER WOULD PUT BACK ANY DUPLICATES. LATER WHEN I TOOK OVER THE GROCERY SHOPPING MY MOTHER WOULD GIVE ME LISTS, AND OFTEN SEVERAL OF THE LISTS HAD DUPLICATE ITEMS.

MOTHER WOULD FIRE THE CAREGIVER ALMOST EVERY TIME SHE CAME
TO THE HOUSE, AND I WOULD REHIRE HER. AFTER FOUR WEEKS OF THIS,
I GAVE IN. IT WAS NOT WORTH THE FIGHTING AT THAT TIME. INSTEAD I
STARTED DOING THE GROCERY SHOPPING WITH MOTHER. AFTER A FEW
TIMES OF THIS, I COULD NOT MANAGE IT. I WAS ALWAYS WORRYING ABOUT
LOSING HER IN THE STORE AND SHE WAS VERY SLOW MOVING BY THEN.
WHAT USED TO TAKE THIRTY MINUTES COULD NOW TAKE AN HOUR TO
ACCOMPLISH.

WHEN I STARTED DOING THE SHOPPING BY MYSELF, I WOULD BUY THINGS
THAT REQUIRED NO COOKING, LIKE PACKAGED TURKEY OR COTTAGE
CHEESE. THESE WERE THINGS MOTHER LIKED SO I HOPED SHE WOULD EAT.
EACH WEEK I WOULD CHECK HER REFRIGERATOR, THROW OUT WHATEVER
WAS NO LONGER FRESH, AND START ALL OVER. SHE DID NOT SEEM TO BE
EATING MUCH, SO I MADE SURE I TOOK HER OUT AT LEAST TWO TIMES A
WEEK FOR MEALS. THERE WERE TIMES WHEN I HAD TO TRAVEL OUT OF
TOWN, AND I WOULD ASK MY FRIENDS, AND HER FRIENDS, TO CALL HER
AND TAKE HER OUT. I WAS ALWAYS WORRYING ABOUT HER, SO I WAS NEVER
ASHAMED ABOUT ASKING FOR HELP.

IN THE SUPPORT GROUPS I ATTENDED, ONE THING THAT I NOTICED WAS
HOW FAMILIES DID NOT LIKE TO ASK FOR HELP. THEY THOUGHT THEY
COULD OR SHOULD DO EVRYTHING THEMSELVES. I HAD NO FAMILY IN
TOWN. I HAD NO CHOICE BUT TO ASK FOR HELP IF I WANTED TO HAVE ANY
SEMBLANCE OF MY OWN LIFE.

AROUND THIS SAME TIME MOTHER STARTED ASKING ME ABOUT HOW
SHE COULD GET HER APARTMENT CLEANED. SHE HAD A CLEANING CREW
COMING IN FOR YEARS BUT SHE HAD TO SCHEDULE THEM. SHE WOULD
FORGET TO CALL THEM. WHEN SHE DID SCHEDULE THEM, SHE WOULD GET
CONFUSED ABOUT HOW TO PAY THEM. THEY DID NOT COME FOR WEEKS AT
A TIME. WHEN I WOULD GO TO THE APT. IT ALWAYS APPEARED CLEAN AND
NEAT SO I WAS NOT WORRYING ABOUT THIS – YET.

I DID START WORRYING ABOUT HER APPEARANCE, HOWEVER. SHE WAS
CANCELLING HER HAIR APPOINTMENTS ON A REGULAR BASIS. SHE
ALWAYS WORE HER HAIR SHORT, AND NEVER KNEW HOW TO MANAGE IT
HERSELF. SHE NEVER WASHED IT HERSELF AS SHE HAD A WEEKLY HAIR
APPOINTMENT. WHEN WE WOULD DO ANY OVERSEAS TRAVELING FOR

WEEKS AT A TIME, HER HAIR JUST WENT UNWASHED, AND ALWAYS LOOKED GOOD. NOW, HOWEVER, IT WAS ALWAYS TOO LONG, AND UNKEMPT. MOTHER WAS ALWAYS VERY POLISHED AND CORRECT. TO SEE HER NOT CARING ABOUT HER APPEARANCE WAS UPSETTING TO ME – AND A RED FLAG.

 SHE STARTED TO WEAR THE SAME TWO TO THREE OUTFITS ALL THE TIME. I WAS NOT CERTAIN IF SHE WAS WASHING ANYTHING, AND EVEN THOUGH SHE WAS NOT GETTING TIRED OF WEARING THE SAME CLOTHES, I WAS GETTING TIRED OF SEEING HER IN THEM. THEY WERE ALWAYS APPROPRIATE BUT JUST REPETITIVE, JUST LIKE OUR CONVERSATIONS. THIS IS SOMETHING I AM JUST REALIZING NOW AS I WRITE THIS. I WOULD OCCASIONALLY SUGGEST SHE CHANGE, AND SHE WAS ALWAYS AGREEABLE BUT WHEN I WOULD SEE HER THE NEXT DAY, SHE WOULD HAVE ONE OF THE ORIGINAL OUTFITS ON. THERE WAS CLEARLY A COMFORT ZONE IN THESE CLOTHES FOR HER. I WAS WRONG TO TRY TO GET HER TO CHANGE.

FOR WHATEVER REASON, SHE DID NOT CANCEL HER MANICURES AS OFTEN AS HER HAIR APPOINTMENTS. SHE HAD ACRYLIC NAILS AND THEY LOOKED PERFECT ALL THE TIME. HER MANICURIST WAS VERY UNDERSTANDING OF THE SITUATION, AND OFTEN TOLD ME SHE THOUGHT I WAS OVER-REACTING, THAT MOTHER SEEMED FINE WHEN SHE WAS THERE.

WHEN I MOVED MOTHER TO FLORIDA A FEW YEARS LATER, I BOUGHT HER NEW CLOTHES. I KEPT SOME OF HER FAVORITE OLD ONES, BUT WANTED HER TO HAVE NEW THINGS. I THOUGHT THEY WOULD MAKE HER FEEL GOOD. I REALIZE NOW THAT THIS WAS MEANT TO REASSURE ME AS WELL. INSTEAD SHE KEPT ASKING ME WHY I HAD MY CLOTHES IN HER CLOSET OR WHOSE CLOTHES WERE IN HER CLOSET. SOME OF THE CLOTHES WERE THINGS I BOUGHT WHEN SHE WAS SHOPPING WITH ME, THINGS SHE HAD TRIED ON. THEY NEVER MANAGED TO BE HERS. BUT I GET AHEAD OF MYSELF.

CHAPTER FIVE
TRAVEL BY CAR

I FELT IT WAS IMPORTANT TO HER TO UNDERSTAND THAT SHE HAD A DISEASE AND THAT MUCH OF WHAT WAS HAPPENING TO HER WAS NOT IN HER CONTROL.

TAKING THE CAR FROM HER WAS ONE OF THE HARDEST THINGS I DID DURING THIS ENTIRE JOURNEY. EVERY TIME WE WENT TO THE DOCTOR HE WOULD ASK ABOUT HER DRIVING. I MADE SURE I DROVE WITH HER AT LEAST ONCE A MONTH TO SEE HOW HER DRIVING WAS. FOR THE MOST PART SHE DID NOT GO MANY PLACES AND ALL OF THE PLACES SHE WENT WERE PLACES SHE HAD BEEN GOING FOR MANY YEARS. THAT DOES NOT MEAN THAT I DID NOT WORRY ABOUT HER. THIS ISSUE OF WHEN AND HOW TO TAKE THE CAR KEYS AWAY IS ONE THAT EVERY FAMILY STRUGGLES WITH AS IT IS THE LAST HOLDOUT OF INDEPENDENCE FOR SOMEONE WITH ALZHEIMER'S.

I WOULD SOMETIMES IN CONVERSATION ASK MOTHER HOW SHE FELT ABOUT GIVING UP HER CAR AND PERHAPS GETTING A DRIVER. SHE HAD A FRIEND WHOSE EYESIGHT WAS NOT GOOD AND THIS FRIEND HAD A FULL TIME DRIVER. IN THEORY MOTHER DID NOT SEEM TO MIND THE IDEA OF A DRIVER; IN REALITY SHE FOUGHT AGAINST IT FOR A LONG TIME. FINALLY CIRCUMSTANCES WERE SUCH THAT I WAS ABLE TO TAKE THE CAR WITHOUT A FIGHT. THIS IS WHAT HAPPENED.

MOTHER CALLED ME TO SAY SHE HAD A FLAT TIRE. THE CAR WAS IN THE GARAGE. SHE ASKED ME WHAT SHE SHOULD DO. I TOLD HER I WOULD TAKE CARE OF IT FOR HER AS I RECOGNIZED THIS AS AN OPPORTUNITY. FOR DAYS I DID NOTHING. SHE DID NOT SEEM TO MISS HAVING THE CAR TO USE. THEN WHEN I FINALLY DID GO THERE, I DID NOT FIND A FLAT TIRE. I NEVER DID LEARN WHY MOTHER THOUGHT SHE HAD A FLAT TIRE. AT THAT POINT IT DID NOT MATTER. I JUST TOOK THE CAR TO MY HOUSE. EVERY ONCE IN AWHILE SHE WOULD ASK ABOUT HER CAR AND I WOULD TELL HER THAT THERE WERE THINGS THAT NEEDED TO BE REPAIRED, THAT WE WERE WAITING FOR A PART TO COME IN AND THAT IT WOULD BE SEVERAL MORE DAYS BEFORE THE CAR COULD BE FIXED.

I HATED LYING TO MOTHER BUT I HATED ARGUING WITH HER MORE. I

LEARNED TO TELL HER THINGS THAT WOULD PACIFY HER. SEVERAL MORE DAYS WENT BY. THEN ONE DAY, WHEN WE WERE TOGETHER, SHE ASKED AGAIN ABOUT THE CAR. I TOLD HER SHE WAS NOT GETTING THE CAR BACK. I TOLD HER SHE HAD ALZHEIMER'S AND THAT IT WAS DANGEROUS FOR HER TO DRIVE. SHE DID NOT UNDERSTAND THIS AT ALL. WHENEVER I TOLD HER SHE HAD ALZHEIMER'S SHE ALWAYS ASKED ME HOW I KNEW THAT. I HAD TO TELL HER SHE HAD BEEN TESTED FOR IT.

I DON'T KNOW THAT SHE EVER BELIEVED ME. I FELT IT WAS IMPORTANT FOR HER TO UNDERSTAND THAT SHE HAD A DISEASE AND THAT MUCH OF WHAT WAS HAPPENING TO HER WAS NOT IN HER CONTROL. I DON'T KNOW HOW MUCH OF THIS SHE EVER COMPREHENDED. IF SHE DID, I DON'T KNOW IF IT MADE IT ANY EASIER FOR HER. I WOULD LIKE TO THINK THAT IT DID.

I WOULD ALSO EXPLAIN TO HER THAT BY HER DRIVING AND HER NOT HAVING HER FULL MEMORY SHE COULD INADVERTANTLY PRESS THE GAS PEDAL INSTEAD OF THE BRAKE, OR THINK THE RED LIGHT MEANT GO. IF SHE HAD ANY ACCIDENT WITH THIS DISEASE AND HURT HERSELF I WOULD NEVER HAVE FORGIVEN MYSELF. IF SHE HAD HURT SOMEONE ELSE IT WOULD HAVE BEEN EVEN WORSE.

SO I HIRED A DRIVER. HE WOULD TAKE HER TO THE BEAUTY SHOP OR TO LUNCH AT THE COUNTRY CLUB OR TO DOCTOR APPOINTMENTS, IF SHE RMEMEBERED TO CALL THE DRIVER. OFTEN THE DRIVER WOULD COME TO PICK HER UP, AND SHE WOULD TELL HIM TO GO AWAY AS SHE HAD CANCELLED THE PARTICULAR APPOINTMENT. SOMETIMES SHE WOULD HAVE AN APPOINTMENT BUT HAD FORGOTTEN TO CALL THE DRIVER. THIS ARRANGEMENT WAS CLEARLY NOT WORKING BUT THERE WAS NO WAY I COULD BE HER FULL TIME CHAUFFEUR OR HER FULL TIME APPOINTMENT SECRETARY. FOR WEEKS I TRIED TO DO SOME OF THE DRIVING AND APPOINTMENT MAKING AND HOPED THAT SHE WOULD DO THE REST.

BY THIS TIME IT WAS ALREADY YEARS INTO THE DISEASE. IT WAS TIME TO MAKE SOME MAJOR CHANGES AND DECISIONS.

CHAPTER SIX
BIRTHDAYS CELEBRATED ON THE ROAD

AT THAT MOMENT I KNEW I DID NOT HAVE MY
MOTHER. SHE WAS ALIVE AND FUNCTIONING
ON SOME LEVELS BUT SHE COULD NOT DO HER
MOTHER THINGS FOR ME.

AS A YOUNG GIRL I THOUGHT THAT BIRTHDAYS WERE THE BEST DAYS,
ESPECIALLY MY BIRTHDAY. I STILL THINK BIRTHDAYS ARE SPECIAL. MY
PARENTS WOULD FUSS OVER ME AND MAKE ME FEEL LIKE A PRINCESS ON
MY BIRTHDAY. THERE WERE ALWAYS PARTIES AND GIFTS, BUT MOST OF ALL
THERE WAS ALWAYS LOTS OF ATTENTION. AS I GOT OLDER, THE BIRTHDAYS
WERE JUST AS IMPORTANT. I FUSSED OVER MY PARENTS ON THEIR
BIRTHDAYS AS WELL AS OVER MY SISTER AND HER KIDS. MY FRIENDS WILL
TELL YOU IF YOU ASK WHAT IS THE MOST IMPORTANT HOLIDAY TO ME,
THAT IT IS MY BIRTHDAY.

WHEN MOTHER TURNED FIFTY, I WAS LIVING IN NEW YORK CITY. MY
FATHER HAD PLANNED A PARTY FOR HER THAT WAS NOT A SURPRISE.
HOWEVER, MY BEING THERE WAS DEFINITELY A SURPRISE. DAD ROLLED ME
INTO THE LUNCHEON IN A HUGE TELEVISION BOX AND THEN HELPED ME
OUT. MOTHER THOUGHT SHE WAS GETTING A NEW TELEVISION SET, AND
INSTEAD SHE GOT ME. THIS WAS TYPICAL OF HOW BIG BIRTHDAYS WERE IN
OUR FAMILY.

MOTHER GAVE ME A LOVELY PARTY WHEN I TURNED FIFTY. MY SISTER AND
NIECE CAME IN FROM OUT OF TOWN FOR IT. FRIENDS BROUGHT STORIES
OF HOW THEY HAD MET ME. THE ENTIRE YEAR WAS ACTUALLY ONE BIG
CELEBRATION BUT THE HIGHLIGHT WAS THE PARTY MOTHER GAVE ME. SHE
WROTE A WONDERFUL POEM AND PLANNED EVERYTHING. IT WAS PERFECT.

WHEN SHE TURNED EIGHTY I GAVE A LUNCHEON AT MY HOUSE FOR HER.
BY THEN MY SISTER HAD DIED AND MY EIGHTEEN YEAR OLD NIECE
COULD NOT COME IN FOR THE PARTY. SOME COUSINS DROVE IN FROM
DETROIT AND SURPRISED HER THE NIGHT BEFORE. SHE SEEMED HAPPY,
BUT CONFUSED. WHEN SHE GOT TO MY HOUSE FOR THE LUNCHEON I WAS
VERY SURPRISED TO SEE WHAT SHE HAD WORN. IT WAS ALMOST LIKE
A HOUSEDRESS, RATHER THAN A NICE LUNCHEON OUTFIT, ESPECIALLY
FOR THE BIRTHDAY GIRL. I DID NOT SAY ANYTHING AND PERHAPS I WAS

THE ONLY ONE THAT EVEN NOTICED. IN FACT, THROUGHOUT THIS ENTIRE PROCESS OF JOURNEYING THROUGH ALZHEIMER'S WITH HER, I FOUND I OFTEN WAS THE ONLY ONE WHO NOTICED THE LITTLE THINGS.
PERHAPS THIS WAS BECAUSE MOTHER AND I WERE VERY CLOSE; PERHAPS IT WAS BECAUSE I WAS PAYING ATTENTION TO EVERYTHING AND SPENDING A LOT OF TIME WITH HER. SOMETIMES IT MADE ME WONDER IF I WAS OVER- REACTING TO LITTLE THINGS. THERE WERE MANY TIMES I DOUBTED MYSELF AS WELL AS MY OBSERVATIONS.

WHEN IT CAME TIME TO THANK EVERYONE AT HER EIGHTIETH BIRTHDAY PARTY FOR BEING THERE AND FOR THE GROUP GIFT, SHE JUST SAID,"THANK YOU". I WAS QUITE SURPRISED. THAT WAS ALL SHE SAID, "THANK YOU". THERE WAS NO POEM AND THERE WERE NO MORE WORDS. BOTH MY MOTHER AND FATHER ALWAYS HAD A POEM FOR EVERY OCCASION. WE HAD A SPECIAL POEM THAT I HAD GIVEN MY FATHER WHEN HE TURNED FIFTY THAT HE USED FOR EVERYTHING IN ADDITION TO WHATEVER POEM HE OR MOTHER WROTE. I HAD READ THAT POEM CALLED COUNT YOUR GARDEN THIS PARTICULAR AFTERNOON. MOTHER SEEMED TO JUST DRIFT THROUGH THE PARTY BUT NOT BE REALLY THERE. OFTEN HER EYES SEEMED GLAZED OVER, AND THIS WAS SOMETHING I BEGAN TO NOTICE WITH SOME FREQUENCY THEREAFTER. THESE ARE THE KIND OF RED FLAGS I NOTICED; EACH FAMILY WILL HAVE THEIR OWN TRADITIONS AND STORIES. ANY CHANGE FROM THOSE IS TO BE LOOKED AT AS A RED FLAG. IT MAY NOT BE A POEM OR A DRESS THAT IS NOT RIGHT, BUT THERE MAY BE SOMETHING SIMILAR THAT YOU CAN SAY, " OH, THAT IS SIMILAR TO WHAT MY LOVED ONE IS DOING, OR NOT DOING". IT WILL ALERT YOU TO START PAYING ATTENTION TO SOME OF THE LITTLE DAILY ACTIONS OR LACK OF ACTIONS.

THEN IT WAS MY FIFTY-FIFTH BIRTHDAY. THIS TIME MOTHER WAS NOT CAPABLE OF PUTTING TOGETHER A PARTY. IT DID NOT EVEN SEEM TO BE A THOUGHT PROCESS FOR HER. SO I MADE MY OWN PARTY. I DID ALL THE PLANNING BUT STILL MADE HER THE HOSTESS. THIS WAS SO HARD TO DO. IT WAS WHEN THE REALITY OF HOW CHANGED HER LIFE AND HOW CHANGED MY LIFE REALLY SET IN. IT WAS SIMILAR TO THE EXPERIENCE I HAD WHEN I HAD SOME MINOR EYE SURGERY. WHEN I WAS FILLING OUT THE FORMS INSTEAD OF PUTTING IN MY MOTHER FOR WHOM TO CONTACT IN AN EMERGENCY, I PUT IN MY BEST FRIEND'S NAME. AT THAT MOMENT I KNEW I DID NOT HAVE MY MOTHER. SHE WAS ALIVE AND FUNCTIONING ON SOME LEVELS BUT SHE COULD NOT DO MOTHER THINGS FOR ME. I WAS,

INSTEAD, DOING MOTHER-LIKE THINGS FOR HER.

I JUST HAD MY SIXTIETH BIRTHDAY. MOTHER HAS BEEN GONE FOR OVER
TWO YEARS. THIS BIRTHDAY WAS HARD WITHOUT HER, BUT MY FIFTY-FIFTH
WAS HARD WITH HER.

CHAPTER SEVEN

FEELING LOST ON THE ROAD

MOTHER WAS A GOOD ATHLETE. WHEN SHE WAS IN HER TEENS SHE STARTED PLAYING GOLF AND CONTINUED PLAYING THROUGHOUT HER LIFE – OR SO SHE THOUGHT.

SHE AND DAD BELONGED TO A COUNTRY CLUB WHERE SHE PLAYED GOLF IN THE SUMMER. SHE HAD A LOCKER IN THE WOMEN'S LOCKER ROOM AND I REMEMBER WHEN I WAS A TEENAGER SHARING IT WITH HER. IT WAS ALWAYS THE SAME LOCKER, IN THE SAME PLACE. A LOT OF MOTHER'S LIFE, IN FACT, WAS THE SAME YEAR AFTER YEAR. HER ROUTINES DID NOT VARY MUCH. IT WAS LIKELY BECAUSE OF THIS THAT WHEN THEY DID VARY SOME, I NOTICED IT AS MUCH AS I DID.

THE LAST FIVE YEARS OF MOTHER'S LIFE IT SEEMED TO ME THAT SHE WAS PLAYING LESS GOLF, BUT TALKING ABOUT IT AS IF SHE WERE STILL PLAYING THE SAME AMOUNT. SHE NO LONGER WAS ENTERING ANY OF THE TOURNAMENTS. OFTEN SHE WOULD NOT FINISH ALL EIGHTEEN HOLES. MOST OF THE WOMEN SHE WAS PLAYING WITH WERE HER AGE AND SO THEY WERE LIKELY JUST AS HAPPY NOT TO FINISH. HOWEVER, IT MEANT THAT THEY COULD NOT TURN IN THEIR SCORES OR KEEP THEIR HANDICAPS CURRENT. IF YOU ARE NOT A GOLFER YOU MAY NOT KNOW WHAT THIS MEANS. BOTTOM LINE IS THAT IT MEANS NO TOURNAMENT PLAY.AT THIS POINT IN HER LIFE THAT DID NOT SEEM TO MATTER TO HER.

THE NEXT TWO SUMMERS AFTER SHE STOPPED PLAYING A FULL EIGHTEEN HOLES I NOTICED THAT SHE WAS PLAYING LESS AND LESS, EVEN THOUGH SHE WOULD STILL TALK AS IF GOLF WERE AN IMPORTANT PART OF HER LIFE. ONCE WE HAD DINNER WITH A JAPANESE BUSINESSMAN WHO WAS IN TOWN. I ALWAYS INCLUDED MOTHER IN MY BUSINESS MEALS WHEN I COULD. SHE AND MY FATHER HAD TRAVELLED TO JAPAN SEVERAL TIMES, AND SHE AND I HAD BEEN THERE A FEW TIMES TOGETHER. GOLF IS VERY POPULAR IN JAPAN AND THIS MAN WAS A KEEN GOLFER. NATURALLY GOLF CAME UP IN THE CONVERSATION. SINCE I DO NOT PLAY GOLF, THERE WAS LITTLE I COULD ADD TO THE CONVERSATION. MOTHER WAS TELLING HIM ABOUT CERTAIN SHOTS AND SCORES THAT I KNEW WERE NOT RECENT. IT WAS ALMOST LIKE WATCHING A MOVIE. OF COURSE, THIS MAN DID NOT KNOW THAT THE STORIES WERE NOT TRUE, AT LEAST NOT TRUE FOR THE TIME PERIOD BEING DISCUSSED. THIS KIND OF CONVERSATION WAS

"NORMAL" FOR US. WE WOULD BE WITH OTHERS AND ONLY I WOULD KNOW THAT WHAT MOTHER WAS TALKING ABOUT WAS SOMETHING IN THE PAST OR SOMETHING IN HER IMAGINATION. YET IT ALWAYS SOUNDED APPROPRIATE AND CURRENT TO WHOMEVER WE WERE WITH.

WHEN THE TIME CAME FOR ME TO TAKE OVER MOTHER'S FINANCIAL AFFAIRS I HAD ALL THE BILLS CHANGED TO MY ADDRESS. I GOT A BILL FROM THE COUNTRY CLUB THAT INCLUDED CHARGES FOR THE LOCKER THAT I KNEW MOTHER WAS NO LONGER USING, AS SHE WAS NO LONGER PLAYING GOLF. I WENT TO THE CLUB AND EMPTIED OUT HER LOCKER, AND CRIED. IT WAS ANOTHER THING I WAS TAKING AWAY FROM HER. THE REALITY OF HER NO LONGER NEEDING HER LOCKER, WHICH SHE HAD FOR SO MANY YEARS, HIT ME VERY HARD. THE COUNTRY CLUB HAD BEEN A PART OF OUR LIVES SINCE I WAS VERY YOUNG. I HAD SHARED THIS LOCKER WITH HER AS A TEEN-AGER. IT WAS ANOTHER DOOR CLOSING. I COULD ALMOST HEAR THE SLAMMING OF THE DOORS AS I CLOSED THE LOCKER DOOR FOR THAT LAST TIME.

THE CHECK BOOK WAS MUCH EASIER TO TAKE FROM HER. SHE HAD BEEN HAVING TROUBLE KEEPING THE CHECK BOOK FOR MONTHS. I BOUGHT HER AN ADDING MACHINE, BUT THAT DID NOT SEEM TO HELP. MOTHER HAD ALWAYS TAKEN CARE OF THE FINANCIAL MATTERS IN THE HOUSE SO SHE KNEW HOW TO DO THIS – OR AT LEAST SHE USED TO KNOW.

OCCASIONALLY SHE WOULD ASK ME TO BALANCE THE CHECK BOOK, WHICH I WOULD DO. THEN ONE DAY SHE CALLED TO SAY SHE COULD NOT BALANCE THE CHECK BOOK - AGAIN -, AND THAT THE BANK WAS SHOWING HER OVERDRAWN. THERE WERE ALL SORTS OF CHARGES ON THE ACCOUNT FROM THE BANK SHE DID NOT UNDERSTAND. I PICKED UP EVERYTHING FROM HER AND TRIED TO FIGURE IT OUT. ACCORDING TO HER CHECKBOOK SHE WAS NOT OVERDRAWN. I FINALLY HAD TO GIVE IT TO OUR ACCOUNTANT TO FIGURE OUT WHAT WAS WRONG. THE ACCOUNTANT HAD NO BETTER LUCK WITH IT.

MY NEXT STEP WAS TO GO TO THE BANK. IT TURNED OUT ONE CHECK, WHICH WE THINK WAS A SOCIAL SECURITY CHECK, WAS IN HER CHECK BOOK BUT HAD NEVER BEEN DEPOSITED. I EXPLAINED TO THE BANK CUSTOMER SERVICE PERSON WHAT I THOUGHT HAD HAPPENED AND ASKED HER TO ELIMINATE THE EXTRA SERVICE CHARGES. I TOLD HER THAT MY MOTHER HAD ALZHEIMER'S. THIS WOMAN DID NOT SEEM TO CARE. I TOLD

HER I WOULD HAVE TO CLOSE THE ACCOUNT IF SHE COULD NOT ELIMINATE THE FEES. MOTHER HAD THIS ACCOUNT FOR OVER FORTY-FIVE YEARS. THE YOUNG LADY IN CUSTOMER SERVICE SAID, "THEN I GUESS YOU WILL HAVE TO CLOSE THE ACCOUNT". THAT IS EXACTLY WHAT I DID.

I MOVED MOTHER'S ACCOUNT INTO THE BANK WHERE I HAD BOTH MY PERSONAL AND BUSINESS ACCOUNTS. I WENT TO THE SOCIAL SECURITY OFFICE AND GOT ALL THE NECESSARY PAPERWORK FOR DIRECT DEPOSITS TO BE MADE. I NEVER GAVE MOTHER BACK HER CHECK BOOK. OCCASIONALLY SHE WOULD ASK FOR THE CHECK BOOK, AND I WOULD JUST TELL HER I WAS TAKING CARE OF IT FOR HER. I THINK SHE MISSED HER INDEPENDENCE BUT WAS ALSO VERY RELIEVED THAT SHE DID NOT HAVE TO WORRY ABOUT THE MONEY AND THE MECHANICS OF THE MONEY.

MOTHER NEVER SEEMED TO NOTICE THAT SHE WAS NO LONGER GETTING BILLS IN THE MAIL. SHE NEVER COMMENTED ON NOT GETTING THE BILLS NOR DID SHE ASK ME IF I WAS GETTING THEM. HER MIND JUST NEVER CONNECTED ABOUT THIS PART OF HER LIFE CHANGING. IN A SENSE THESE KINDS OF CHANGES CAN BE HARDER ON THE FAMILY THAN ON THE INDIVIDUAL WITH ALZHEIMER'S AS THE FAMILY UNDERSTANDS WHAT THE CHANGES MEAN FOR THE FUTURE.

CHAPTER EIGHT
ROADS OPENING THROUGH SUPPORT GROUPS

THERE IS NO ROAD MAP FOR THIS JOURNEY.

BECAUSE MY MOTHER WAS AN ONLY CHILD AND VERY INDEPENDENT, I DID NOT THINK SHE WOULD GO TO THE SUPPORT GROUPS OFFERED BY THE ALZHEIMER'S ASSOCIATION. I KNEW I NEEDED SOME HELP AND NEEDED TO KNOW MORE ABOUT WHAT THE FUTURE WOULD HOLD. SHE DID NOT FEEL THE NEED TO KNOW. AT THIS POINT SHE DID NOT ACKNOWLEDGE OUT LOUD THAT THERE WAS A PROBLEM. I SUSPECT FROM THE BEGINNING OF THIS DISEASE THAT MOTHER KNEW SOMETHING WAS NOT QUITE RIGHT BUT IT WOULD NOT HAVE BEEN HER WAY TO DISCUSS IT OR TO SPECULATE.

HOWEVER, SHE DID COME TO A SERIES OF MEETINGS WITH ME EVENTUALLY. SHE NEVER LIKED THEM AND NEVER FELT THEY WERE HELPFUL. SHE WOULD COMPLAIN ABOUT THE MEETINGS AND ABOUT THE PEOPLE AT THEM, BUT SHE CONTINUED TO COME WITH ME.

I DID NOT ASK HER TO COME WITH ME AGAIN. I WENT TO A FEW MORE SESSIONS MYSELF AND ALWAYS LEARNED SOMETHING. ONE SESSION THERE WAS A DOCTOR SPEAKING ABOUT DEPRESSION WHICH OFTEN ACCOMMPANIES THIS DISEASE. HE MENTIONED THAT PUTTING PATIENTS ON AN ANTI-DEPRESSANT CAN MAKE THEM HAPPIER BUT CAN MAKE THEIR MEMORY WORSE. THAT PRETTY MUCH SUMMED ALZHEIMER'S UP FOR ME. FOR EVERY DECISION THAT I MADE, THERE WERE CONSEQUENCES. I ALWAYS HAD TO DECIDE WHICH WAS THE BEST THAT COULD HAPPEN AND WHICH WAS THE WORST. I WAS ALWAYS SECOND GUESSING MYSELF.

THERE IS NO ROAD MAP FOR THIS JOURNEY. YOU CAN NEVER BE SURE THAT YOU ARE ON THE RIGHT ROAD. YOU ALWAYS WONDER ABOUT THE ROAD NOT TAKEN. IF YOU MAKE ONE DECISION THERE ARE CERTAIN CONSEQUENCES; IF YOU MAKE THE OTHER CHOICE THERE WOULD POSSIBLY BE OTHER RESULTS. YOU NEVER KNOW FOR SURE. IT IS A MOST FRUSTRATING EXPERIENCE FOR THE CAREGIVER. YOU LOSE SOME SELF-ESTEEM ALONG THE WAY, AS YOU NEVER REALLY KNOW IF YOU MADE THE RIGHT DECISIONS.

WATCHING SOMEONE YOU LOVE LOSE HER/HIS MEMORY IS AWFUL. WATCHING THAT PERSON BE DEPRESSED IS AWFUL. IF HER/HIS MEMORY

GETS WORSE THERE ARE FEWER THINGS SHE/HE CAN DO ALONE. HE MAY NOT BE ABLE TO LIVE ALONE. IF SHE IS DEPRESSED SHE MAY NOT BE HAPPY LIVING ALONE. YOU CAN SEE WHERE I AM GOING WITH THIS. IN CIRCLES AND SPIRALS. THAT IS WHAT IT FEELS LIKE TO BE A CAREGIVER.

ONCE WHEN MOTHER AND I HAD JUST LEFT HER APPOINTMENT WITH DR. WHITEHOUSE, SHE SAID TO ME "THIS MUST BE VERY HARD FOR YOU". WHEN I ASKED HER WHY SHE REPLIED "BECAUSE YOU ARE NOW AN ONLY CHILD WITH AN ONLY PARENT AND I KNOW WHAT THAT IS LIKE". AS MENTIONED EARLIER, HER FATHER HAD DIED WHEN SHE WAS ONLY EIGHTEEN AND SHE HAD TO LOOK AFTER HER MOTHER. DURING THIS CONVERSATION MOTHER WENT ON TO SAY THAT HER MOTHER WAS NEUROTIC. I LAUGHED AT THIS COMMENT, AS I HAD NEVER HEARD HER SAY ANYTHING LIKE THAT ABOUT HER MOTHER. I THINK WHEN SHE SAID SHE HAD TO CARE FOR HER MOTHER IT WAS MORE ON AN EMOTIONAL LEVEL THAN FINANCIALLY. I ACTUALLY DON'T KNOW, AND THERE IS NO WAY TO GET THIS QUESTION, OR ANY OTHER QUESTIONS ANSWERED NOW. I REGRET NOT ASKING MORE QUESTIONS AND NOT HAVING THE ANSWERS WHEN I HAD THE OPPORTUNITY TO DO SO.

I FOUND THE SUPPORT GROUPS TO BE PART OF MY SALVATION. TO KNOW THAT OTHERS ARE GOING THROUGH SOME OF THE SAME THINGS AND THAT THEY CARE ABOUT YOU AND YOUR EXPERIENCES IS DEFINITELY HELPFUL. IN MY CASE, I HAD NO HUSBAND, NO CHILDREN, AND NO SIBLINGS TO DISCUSS ANY OF THIS WITH OR TO HELP WITH ANY OF THE DECISION MAKING. THAT WAS PAINFUL AT TIMES AND AT OTHER TIMES IT WAS FREEING. I SAW IN THE SUPPORT GROUPS HOW FAMILIES WOULD DISAGREE; I ALSO SAW HOW THEY WOULD BE THERE FOR EACH OTHER.
IN A WAY, THE SUPPORT GROUP MEMBERS BECAME MY SUBSTITUTE FAMILY WHEN I NEEDED THEM.

CHAPTER NINE
ASKING FOR DIRECTIONS

AT THE FIRST SUPPORT GROUP I WENT TO I MET A VOLUNTEER WHO HAD GONE THROUGH THE PROCESS WITH HER DAD. SHE APPEARED TO BE SO CALM AND GROUNDED. WE BECAME SOMEWHAT FRIENDLY OVER THE SESSIONS BUT I DID NOT SEE HER AGAIN UNTIL I STARTED MY THIRD SUPPORT SERIES. I FOUND OUT THEN THAT SHE WAS A YOGA TEACHER, WHICH EXPLAINED TO ME HER STATE OF AWARENESS AND CALM. I HAD TRIED SOME YOGA CLASSES OFF AND ON OVER THE YEARS BUT HAD NEVER REALLY LIKED THEM. MY BOYFRIEND HAD BEEN DOING YOGA FOR YEARS AND KEPT TELLING ME I SHOULD TRY IT AGAIN. MEETING AND GETTING TO KNOW THIS WOMAN CONVINCED ME THAT I SHOULD CONSIDER YOGA AS A WAY OF STAYING CALM AND BETTER HANDLING THE STRESS OF MY MOTHER'S ALZHEIMER'S. ACTUALLY I STARTED DOING YOGA WITHOUT KNOWING FULLY THAT I WAS DOING IT.

I HAD PLANNED A TREKKING TRIP TO NEPAL.THIS WAS STILL SOMEWHAT EARLY ON IN MY MOTHER'S MEMORY LOSS, AND I WAS COMFORTABLE LEAVING HER THEN. HOWEVER, THIS WAS THE FIRST MAJOR TRIP OVERSEAS THAT I WAS MAKING WITHOUT MY MOTHER. THE REALITY OF THAT WAS VERY SAD FOR ME. I BEGAN TO RECOGNIZE THAT WHILE ALZHEIMER'S TAKES MANY THINGS AWAY FROM THE PERSON THAT HAS THE DISEASE, IT ALSO TAKES SO MANY THINGS AWAY FROM THE FAMILY MEMBERS AS WELL. IT WAS NOT JUST THE FACT THAT MOTHER COULD NO LONGER TRAVEL WITH ME ON THESE ADVENTURE TRIPS; IT WAS THAT I COULD NOT EVEN DISCUSS THE TRIP WITH HER AS SHE WAS NOT RETAINING NEW MEMORIES OR NEW INFORMATION.

I WANTED TO BE SURE I WOULD BE ABLE TO HANDLE THE ALTITUDE OF NEPAL. WHEN MOTHER AND I HAD BEEN IN TIBET 15 YEARS EARLIER, I HAD GOTTEN ALTITUDE SICKNESS. I ASKED SALLY, MY FRIEND FROM THE SUPPORT GROUP THAT TAUGHT YOGA, TO HELP TEACH ME THE PROPER WAY TO BREATHE. SHE CAME TO THE HOUSE FOR SEVERAL WEEKS BEFORE MY TRIP AND WORKED WITH ME, DOING LOTS OF DIFFERENT BREATHING EXERCISES. TOWARDS THE END OF THE LESSONS, I FINALLY REALIZED THAT WHAT WE WERE DOING WAS YOGA, AND THAT WITH THE RIGHT TEACHER IT WAS SOMETHING THAT I COULD LIKE. IT WAS ALSO A VERY CALMING EXPERIENCE, ONE THAT HELPED ME COPE WITH THE STRESS OF MY MOTHER'S ILLNESS.

WHEN I CAME BACK FROM NEPAL, I SIGNED UP FOR A YOGA CLASS THAT A FRIEND OF SALLY'S WAS TEACHING. THOSE OF YOU READING THIS NOW MAY WONDER WHY I AM INCLUDING THIS IN THIS STORY. PLEASE KEEP READING. THIS IS A PART OF MY PERSONAL JOURNEY AND ONE THAT I HOPE WILL INSPIRE YOU.

THE YOGA TEACHER WAS JAN HAUSENSTEIN, WHO IS ONE OF THE MOST GENTLE AND WONDERFUL WOMEN I HAVE HAD THE PRIVILEGE TO KNOW. I LOVED HER CLASSES. DURING THIS SAME TIME SALLY KANE WAS STARTING TO DO SOME RELAXATION WORK WITH BOTH THE CAREGIVERS AND THE PERSON WITH ALZHEIMER AT THE SUPPORT GROUPS. MOSTLY SHE WAS USING VISUALIZATION AND MUSIC BUT ALSO A LITTLE YOGA AND BREATHING TECHNIQUES.

I THINK IT WAS BECAUSE OF MY TAKING THE YOGA CLASSES WITH JAN AND KNOWING SALLY THAT I CAME UP WITH THE IDEA OF STARTING SOME YOGA CLASSES SPECIFICALLY GEARED TOWARDS THE CAREGIVERS. I KNEW HOW MUCH PRACTICING YOGA WAS HELPING ME COPE AND I WANTED TO HELP OTHERS GOING THROUGH THE SAME JOURNEY. THE PROBLEM WITH THIS WAS TWOFOLD. ONE: THERE WAS NO MONEY AT THE ALZHEIMER'S ASSOCIATION TO PAY FOR A PROGRAM LIKE THIS AND TWO: YOGA FOR INDIVIDUALS WITH ALZHEIMER'S OR THEIR CAREGIVERS WAS STILL CONSIDERED A SOMEWHAT RADICAL APPROACH.

ONE NIGHT BEFORE YOGA CLASS JAN AND I WERE TRYING TO FIGURE OUT A WAY TO MAKE THIS POTENTIAL YOGA PROGRAM WORK. WHAT I DID NOT KNOW AT THE TIME, AND DID NOT KNOW FOR MANY MONTHS, WAS THAT JAN'S DAD HAD ALZHEIMER'S WHEN HE DIED, AND SHE KNEW FIRSTHAND HOW YOGA COULD HELP THE CAREGIVERS. IN THE COURSE OF THE CONVERSATION I CAME UP WITH THE IDEA OF TRYING TO GET SOME CORPORATE SPONSERS. THEN AS I WAS GOING THROUGH THE YOGA POSITIONS AND MY MIND WAS CALM, I REALIZED THAT I HAD THE MONIES TO MAKE THIS HAPPEN, OR AT LEAST MY MOTHER DID.

MOTHER HAD A FUND WITH JEWISH UNITED FUND IN WHICH SHE COULD DESIGNATE WHERE THE MONEY WENT AS LONG AS IT WAS A CHARITY. AS LONG AS SHE WAS ALIVE, SHE HAD THIS RIGHT. UPON HER DEATH, JEWISH UNITED FUND COULD SPEND THE MONEY AS THEY CHOSE. SINCE I HAD POWER OF ATTORNEY FOR ALL MOTHER'S THINGS BY THIS TIME, I

COULD DESIGNATE MONIES TO GO TO THE ALZHEIMER'S ASSOCIATION. THE NEXT DAY I CALLED JEWISH UNITED FUND TO FIND OUT HOW MUCH MONEY WAS STILL IN THE FUND, CALLED SALLY OLLERTON AT ALZHEIMERS ASSOCIATION TO ASK IF WE COULD SET UP A MEETING WITH WHOMEVER WE NEEDED TO APPROVE THIS PROJECT, AND WE WERE OFF AND RUNNING.

WE WERE ABLE TO START THIS FUND AT THE ALZHEIMER'S ASSOCIATION IN MOTHER'S HONOR FOR PROJECTS SPECIFICALLY DESIGNED TO AID CAREGIVERS. THE FUND STARTED WITH ALMOST $24,000 IN AUGUST OF 1999. I FELT THAT AT LAST SOMETHING GOOD WAS COMING OUT OF SOMETHING BAD.

IN NOVEMBER1999 THE FIRST SERIES OF "RELAX AND RENEW" WAS HELD. IT WAS A FIVE-WEEK SERIES. ELEVEN PERSONS WITH MEMORY LOSS AND THEIR FAMILIES (ANOTHER 15 PEOPLE) CAME TO THESE MEETINGS. THE SERIES COST CLOSE TO $3500 TO DESIGN AND RUN, AND I FELT THAT THE MONEY WAS BEING PUT TO VERY GOOD USE. FAMILY MEMBERS WERE TAUGHT HOW TO DO SOME RELAXATION POSES OF YOGA, AND HOW TO BREATHE DEEPLY AND SLOWLY IN ORDER TO RELAX. THEY WERE TAUGHT HOW TO STAY CALM IF THEIR PERSON BECAME AGITATED AND HOW TO CALM DOWN THEIR LOVED ONE. IT WAS A GOOD BEGINNING.

ANOTHER "RELAX AND RENEW" SERIES WAS HELD IN APRIL OF 2000 WITH 30 PEOPLE ATTENDING. THEN IN SEPTEMBER 2000 THE ALZHEIMER'S ASSOCIATION RECEIVED A GRANT SPECIFICALLY FOR THE "RELAX AND RENEW" PROGRAM FROM MT. SINAI COMMUNITY PARTNERS FOR $5000.00.

IN MARCH 2001 THE "RELAX AND RENEW" PROGRAM WAS REDISIGNED IN RESPONSE TO THE NEEDS OF THE FAMILIES AND WAS RENAMED "ACTIVITIES TOGETHER". THIS PROGRAM WAS ACTUALLY PRESENTED TO THE ALZHEIMER'S ASSOCIATION NATIONAL CONFERENCE IN JULY 2001. BY THE END OF SEPTEMBER 2001, SIXTY FAMILIES COMPRISING 132 INDIVIDUALS HAD BEEN SERVED BY THE PROGRAM. NOW THE PROGRAM HAS BEEN INCORPORATED INTO THE ONGOING SUPPORT GROUP SERIES CALLED "STAYING CONNECTED". (MORE INFORMATION CAN BE HAD FROM THE ALZHEIMER'S ASSOCIATION IN CLEVELAND. PHONE: 216-721-8457 DONATIONS CAN BE MADE TO THE RUTH SILBERMAN FUND AT THE ALZHEIMER'S ASSOCIATION CLEVELAND AREA CHAPTER, 12200 FAIRHILL ROAD, CLEVELAND, OH 44120).

DURING THIS PROCESS, SALLY OLLERTON, WHO IS A SOCIAL WORKER WITH THE ALZHEIMER'S ASSOCIATION, WORKED WITH ME TO GET THE SESSIONS GOING AND INCORPORATED INTO REGULAR MEETINGS WITH THE FAMILIES. SALLY IS A VERY GENTLE AND KIND WOMAN. SHE IS PERFECT IN HER JOB, WONDERFUL WITH THE FAMILIES AND WITH THE PERSONS WITH MEMORY LOSS. SOMEHOW SHE ALWAYS KNOWS THE RIGHT THING TO SAY AND THE RIGHT COURSE OF ACTION TO TAKE. OVER A YEAR AFTER MOTHER PASSED AWAY SALLY WAS COMING TO VISIT ME. I MENTIONED THE VISIT TO A FRIEND IN CLEVELAND WHO SAID MY FRIENDSHIP WITH SALLY WAS A GIFT FROM MY MOTHER. I LOVE THAT THOUGHT PROCESS. HAD IT NOT BEEN FOR MOTHER'S HAVING ALZHEIMER'S, I WOULD NOT HAVE MET SALLY NOR WOULD I HAVE SET UP THE FUND HONORING MY MOTHER. BOTH ARE TREASURED GIFTS FROM MY MOTHER AND I EXPECT FOR THOSE OF YOU READING THESE WORDS, THERE ARE GIFTS THAT YOUR LOVED ONE WITH MEMORY LOSS IS GIVING TO YOU AS WELL – SOMETIMES YOU JUST HAVE TO READJUST YOUR THINKING TO FIND THEM.

HAVING SALLY OLLERTON IN MY LIFE TO TALK WITH AND TO ASK FOR GUIDANCE IN MY DECISION- MAKING CONCERNING MY MOTHER WAS A TRUE LIFELINE AND BLESSING. I NEVER FELT ALONE DURING THIS PROCESS. I HAD TOTAL BELIEF IN HER EXPERIENCE AND CARING. YES, I WAS ALWAYS THE FINAL DECISION MAKER, BUT SALLY ALWAYS MADE IT EASIER FOR ME TO MAKE THOSE HARD DECISIONS. I HOPE YOU ARE LUCKY ENOUGH TO HAVE A SALLY IN YOUR LIFE DURING THIS DIFFICULT JOURNEY INTO THE WORLD OF ALZHEIMER'S.

CHAPTER TEN

TRAVELING WITH THE GRANDCHILDREN

IT WAS AS IF SHE HAD BECOME A VIEWER OF LIFE RATHER THAN A PARTICIPANT.

HOW DO YOU EXPLAIN TO YOUNG CHILDREN, EVEN YOUNG TEENAGERS, THAT THEIR GRANDMOTHER HAS ALZHEIMER'S? MOTHER DID NOT SEE HER GRANDCHILDREN MORE THAN A FEW TIMES A YEAR, BUT SHE CALLED THEM OFTEN. I SAW THEM EVEN LESS' AS I COULD NOT MAKE THE TRIPS TO NASHVILLE, TENNESEE WHERE THEY LIVED. THEY USUALLY DID NOT GET TO CLEVELAND MORE THAN ONCE OR TWICE A YEAR. MY SISTER WAS ALREADY GONE AND SO SHE COULD NOT HELP IN EXPLAINING WHAT WAS HAPPENING TO THEIR GRANDMOTHER. I HAD THE TASK OF TRYING TO HELP THEM UNDERSTAND WHAT WAS GOING ON.

TO THINK AT THEIR AGES (ASHLEY WAS 13 AND JARED 12) THEY WOULD NOT NOTICE ANY PROBLEMS WITH THE LITTLE BIT OF CONTACT THEY HAD WITH MOTHER, WHOM THEY CALLED GG FOR GORGEOUS GRANDMOTHER, WAS NAÏVE. OF COURSE THEY NOTICED, AND THEY CALLED ME. IT SEEMS THAT MOTHER WAS CALLING THEM MORE THAN I REALIZED, SOMETIMES SEVERAL TIMES A NIGHT, OR SEVERAL DAYS IN A ROW. IN ALL CASES, SHE DID NOT REMEMBER SHE HAD JUST TALKED WITH THEM. I TOLD ASHLEY AND JARED THAT GG'S CALLING THEM REPEATEDLY AND ALSO REPEATING THE EXACT CONVERSATION WAS LIKE WATCHING THE ACTOR BILL MURRAY IN THE MOVIE GROUNDHOG DAY. HE WOKE UP EVERY DAY TO REPEAT THE EXACT SAME EVENTS, TO HAVE THE EXACT SAME DAY. MOTHER'S PHONE CONVERSATIONS WERE OFTEN LIKE THAT. SHE DID IT WITH ME AS WELL. WE WOULD HAVE A PHONE CONVERSATION FOR A FEW MINUTES AND THEN SHE WOULD CALL ME A FEW MINUTES OR A FEW HOURS LATER, AND WE WOULD HAVE THE SAME CONVERSATION – AGAIN.

THIS WAS SCARY FOR THEM. THEY HAD NO LIFE EXPERIENCE WITH ALZHEIMER'S AND DID NOT KNOW WHAT WAS HAPPENING TO THEIR GRANDMOTHER. I TOLD THEM SHE WAS LOSING SOME OF HER SHORT TERM MEMORY, WHICH EXPLAINED THE FREQUENT CALLS TO THEM. I ALSO TRIED TO REASSURE THEM THAT SHE WOULD NOT FORGET THEM. AT THE STAGE SHE WAS AT I WAS HOPING THAT WAS A GOOD BET. AS IT TURNED OUT IT WAS. A FEW MONTHS BEFORE MOTHER DIED, SHE DID START TO FORGET WHO I WAS HOWEVER. SHE WOULD CALL MY HOUSE AND ASK ME IF I KNEW

WHERE "LYN" WAS. WHEN I WOULD REPLY THAT I WAS LYN, SHE ALWAYS LAUGHED IT OFF AND SAID OF COURSE. I KNEW THEN THAT WE WERE GETTING CLOSE TO ANOTHER STAGE OF THE JOURNEY OF THIS DISEASE – AND WHILE I MISS MY MOTHER EVERY DAY, I AM SO GRATEFUL THAT WE NEVER GOT TO THOSE STAGES OF SUCH SEVERE MEMORY LOSS THAT THE PERSON NO LONGER RECOGNIZES FAMILY MEMBERS. GOING THROUGH THE FINAL STAGES OF ALZHEIMER'S IS JUST BEYOND HORRIBLE FOR ALL CONCERNED.

ASHLEY AND JARED WERE OLD ENOUGH TO CALL ME ON THEIR OWN AND COMMUNICATE THEIR FEARS AND CONCERNS. THEY WOULD ALSO TELL ME WHAT MY MOTHER WAS SAYING OR DOING. THIS ACTUALLY HELPED THE THREE OF US TO BECOME CLOSER. WE SURROUNDED MY MOTHER AS PROTECTIVELY WITH LOVE AS WE COULD. I EXPLAINED TO THEM THAT THEY SHOULD NOT SAY TO HER WHEN SHE CALLED THE SECOND OR THIRD OR FOURTH TIME IN A NIGHT, "GG, YOU JUST CALLED OR YOU CALLED ALREADY" OR ANYTHING LIKE THAT. INSTEAD I ENCOURAGED THEM TO TREAT IT AS A GAME AND TO HAVE THE CONVERSATION AGAIN – AND AGAIN. I KNOW THIS WAS NOT EASY FOR THEM, BUT THEY DID IT AS BEST THEY COULD.

THERE WERE MANY TIMES, ESPECIALLY AS THE DISEASE PROGRESSED, THAT MOTHER'S EYES WOULD GLAZE OVER. SHE WOULD SEEM TO GO AWAY TO HER OWN SPECIAL SPOT, NOT TO BE THERE WITH ME. THIS WAS SCARY, ESPECIALLY WHEN IT FIRST STARTED TO HAPPEN. HOWEVER, MY NIECE AND NEPHEW WERE STILL ABLE TO HAVE SOME GOOD TIMES WITH HER, TO HAVE MEALS TOGETHER WHEN THEY VISITED, OR GO SHOPPING OR DO MOST NORMAL THINGS. AFTER THE FIRST FEW YEARS OF MOTHER HAVING THIS DISEASE, I COULD NOT LET HER TRAVEL ON HER OWN TO VISIT THE GRANDCHILDREN IN THEIR HOME. WHEN THEY WERE VISITING US IN CLEVELAND AND IN THE CAR WITH MOTHER, I WORRIED ABOUT THEM AND ABOUT HER. I STARTED HAVING THEM STAY IN MY HOUSE MORE THAN WITH HER, AND THEN REVERSING THAT SO THAT THEY COULD ALMOST BE BABYSITTING HER WHILE THEY WERE IN TOWN. THEY WERE KEEPING HER COMPANY AS SHE WAS HAVING LESS AND LESS OF A SOCIAL LIFE. THROUGHOUT IT ALL THEY WERE TROUPERS. I KNOW IT WAS DIFFICULT FOR THEM TO HAVE THE SAME CONVERSATION OVER AND OVER AGAIN WITH HER. THIS REPETITIVENESS WAS THE MOST NOTICEABLE THING ABOUT MOTHER'S DISEASE AND IT COULD BE VERY ANNOYING. YET THEY STILL WANTED TO VISIT HER, SPEND TIME WITH HER AND LOVE HER.

THE PROCESS MOTHER WENT THROUGH WAS NOT NECESSARILY TYPICAL OF THE JOURNEY MOST WITH THIS DISEASE TAKE. SHE NEVER GOT "SUNDOWNERS" WHICH IS A FREQUENT RESULT OF ALZHEIMER'S. THIS IS WHEN THE ALZHEIMER PATIENT GETS MORE AGITATED AS THE SUN GOES DOWN. MOTHER NEVER GOT MEAN; SHE NEVER GOT PARANOID. WHAT SHE DID GET WAS KINDER. SHE WAS NICER AND MORE APPRECIATIVE AND MORE VERBAL ABOUT THIS APPRECIATION. WE WERE NEVER A VERY VERBAL FAMILY WHEN IT CAME TO EXPRESSING EMOTIONS OR OUR LOVE FOR EACH OTHER. WE USED POEMS AND LETTERS AND CARDS FOR THAT BUT WE DID NOT USE WORDS SPOKEN OUT LOUD VERY OFTEN. SO ON A CERTAIN LEVEL, I WAS STARTING TO ENJOY MY MOTHER MORE, AND ASHLEY AND JARED WERE ENJOYING THEIR GRANDMOTHER MORE AS SHE WAS BECOMING WARMER AND KINDER TO THEM AS WELL. I KNOW IT IS IRONIC THAT THIS HAPPENED, AND I ALSO AM THANKFUL, AS MY LAST SEVERAL MONTHS WITH MOTHER, WHILE STRESSFUL, WERE AT LEAST LOVING ONES.

THIS IS NOT TYPICAL OF WHAT HAPPENS TO THE PERSONALITIES OF MOST PEOPLE WITH ALZHEIMERS. I HAVE A GOOD FRIEND WHOSE MOTHER HAS HAD THIS DISEASE FOR SEVERAL YEARS. SHE DESCRIBES HER MOTHER AS THE "MOTHER OF ALL MOTHERS", MEANING SHE WAS ALWAYS THERE FOR MY FRIEND, ALWAYS INTERESTED IN HER ACTIVITIES, HER WORRIES, HER LIFE. NOW HER MOTHER SHOWS NO INTEREST IN HER LIFE, HER GRANDDAUGHTER'S LIFE OR ANYONE'S LIFE. SHE HAS BECOME MEAN; SHE SAYS MEAN THINGS TO MY FRIEND ALL THE TIME NOW. MY FRIEND KNOWS THAT SHE HAS ALREADY LOST THE MOTHER SHE HAD.

CHAPTER ELEVEN
MOVING TO FLORIDA

AS THE MONTHS PROGRESSED, MOTHER HAD LESS AND LESS OF A SOCIAL LIFE. MOTHER'S BEST FRIEND WAS BUSY CARING FOR HER HUSBAND WHO WAS ILL. MOTHER DID NOT HAVE MANY FRIENDS THAT SHE SPENT MUCH TIME WITH BESIDES HER CARD LADIES ON SATURDAYS. MOTHER'S FRIENDS DID NOT STOP IN ON EACH OTHER AT THEIR HOUSES OR TALK DAILY. THEY DID NOT "PLAY" TOGETHER. MANY OF THEM HAD HEALTH PROBLEMS AND COULD NOT DRIVE, ESPECIALLY AT NIGHT. THIS REALLY ELIMINATED A LOT OF ACTIVITIES. MANY OF HER FRIENDS JUST COULD NOT DEAL WITH MOTHER'S CONSTANTLY REPEATING EVERYTHING NOR COULD THEY ACCEPT THE CONSEQUENCES OF THE DISEASE. SO SLOWLY MOTHER WAS MORE AND MORE BY HERSELF. AT TIMES THIS MADE ME FEEL "RESPONSIBLE" FOR HER SOCIAL LIFE. I TRIED TO BE WITH HER OFTEN, AND ALWAYS INCLUDED HER IN ANY ACTIVITIES OF MINE THAT I THOUGHT SHE MIGHT ENJOY. I WAS, HOWEVER, STARTING TO RESENT AND RESIST BEING HER ONLY SOCIAL LIFE.

MOTHER STILL HAD THE FANTASY THAT SHE PLAYED GOLF REGULARLY IN THE SUMMERS, THAT SHE PLAYED CARDS EVERY SATURDAY AND THAT SHE HAD AN ACTIVE SOCIAL LIFE. HER LIFE USED TO BE LIKE THAT. IT WAS NOT HOW IT WAS ANYMORE. OF COURSE ONE COULD QUESTION WHOSE REALITY WAS THE REAL REALITY. JUST BECAUSE SOME OF HER CURRENT THOUGHT PROCESS WAS FANTASY DID NOT MAKE IT ANY LESS REAL TO HER.

 I DECIDED TO SEE WHAT ASSISTED LIVING FACILITIES WERE AVAILABLE IN FLORIDA. I LOOKED AT TWO. I WANTED TO SPEND THE WINTERS IN FLORIDA, AND I COULD NOT/WOULD NOT LEAVE MOTHER IN CLEVELAND WHILE I WAS IN FLORIDA. SHE HAD NO SOCIAL LIFE IN CLEVELAND. I DID NOT THINK MOVING HER WOULD BE HARMFUL. I ACTUALLY THOUGHT IT MIGHT BE A POSITIVE MOVE FOR HER AS SHE COULD BE OUTSIDE MOST OF THE YEAR. MY COUSIN MARGIE, WHOM MOTHER WAS VERY CLOSE WITH, LIVES NEARBY IN FLORIDA DURING THE WINTER MONTHS AND WOULD BE HERE TO SEE HER REGULARLY. MARGIE WOULD BE OF SOME HELP TO ME AS WELL. I KNEW BY THIS TIME HOW VITAL IT IS TO HAVE SOME BACK UP SUPPORT.

ONE OF THE FACILITIES I LOOKED AT WAS SO BEAUTIFUL I WAS READY TO MOVE IN MYSELF. IT WAS LIKE A WONDERFUL COUNTRY CLUB, WITH ALL

SORTS OF ACTIVITIES, A LOVELY POOL AREA, A BEAUTIFUL COURTYARD AND WONDERFUL STAFF. I COULD MOVE MOTHER INTO A CORNER UNIT AT THE END OF A HALLWAY. HER CONDO IN CLEVELAND WAS ALSO A CORNER UNIT A THE END OF A HALLWAY. I WAS HOPING THIS WOULD FEEL FAMILIAR TO MOTHER BECAUSE OF THE PLACEMENT OF THE UNIT. ANY PATTERNS THAT WERE LONG TERM PATTERNS, I THOUGHT, MIGHT BE EASIER FOR HER TO MAINTAIN IN ORDER TO FUNCTION MORE ON HER OWN. NO ONE ELSE HAD LIVED IN THE UNIT AS THE FACILITY WAS ONLY TWO YEARS OLD AT THE TIME. I THOUGHT ALL OF THESE THINGS WERE POSITIVE.

 IN MOTHER'S CONDO IN CLEVELAND SHE USED TO SPEND SOME TIME LOOKING OUT THE APARTMENT WINDOWS THAT FACED A FREEWAY. I KNEW THIS ONLY BECAUSE SHE WOULD TELL ME ABOUT THE TRAFFIC ON THE FREEWAY. IT WAS AS IF SHE HAD BECOME A VIEWER OF LIFE RATHER THAN A PARTICIPANT. THE UNIT IN THE ASSISTED LIVING FACILITY OVERLOOKED A PRETTY SHOPPING CENTER AND A MAIN STREET SO MOTHER WOULD BE ABLE TO LOOK OUT HER WINDOW AT ACTIVITY. I THOUGHT THIS WOULD PLEASE HER. THE FACT THAT SHE WAS MOVING FROM A LARGE TWO BEDROOMS, THREE BATH CONDO TO A SMALL ONE- BEDROOM, ONE BATH APARTMENT WAS A CONCERN. HOWEVER, I KNEW THE MOVE WAS NECESSARY. MOTHER WAS NO LONGER CAPABLE OF TAKING CARE OF HER LARGE CONDO. I DID NOT EVEN REALIZE AT THE TIME HOW LITTLE SHE WAS CARING FOR THE CONDO – OR EVEN OF HERSELF.

IN ORDER FOR MOTHER TO MOVE INTO THIS FACILITY, THE DIRECTOR OF MARKETING AND SOME OF THE OTHER STAFF MEMBERS HAD TO MEET MOTHER. THEY WANTED TO BE SURE THAT SHE WAS ABLE TO CARE FOR HERSELF ENOUGH TO BE IN THE FACILITY. THIS WAS AN ASSISTED LIVING FACILITY, NOT INDEPENDENT LIVING AS MOTHER BY THIS TIME NEEDED HELP WITH MEDICINES AND GETTING TO MEALS. I MADE ARRANGEMENTS FOR US TO VISIT MY COUSIN MARGIE IN ORDER TO HAVE MOTHER'S INTERVIEW. THROUGHOUT THE ENTIRE TRIP MOTHER WAS CONFUSED. WHILE WE WERE AT THE FACILITY, WHICH SHE DID ACKNOWLEDGE WAS BEAUTIFUL, MOTHER WAS AT HER BEST. I WAS NEVER SURE HOW SHE COULD PULL OFF SEEMING SO NORMAL IN A NEW SOCIAL SITUATION, BUT SHE CONTINUED TO DO THAT TILL THE END. MAYBE IT WAS BECAUSE THE SOCIAL SITUATIONS WERE OFTEN SHORT TIME ENCOUNTERS. THIS FACILITY DID NOT TAKE PERSONS WITH ALZHEIMER'S SO I WAS NATURALLY NERVOUS ABOUT MOTHER'S BEHAVIOR DURING THE INTERVIEW. THERE WOULD HAVE BEEN NO WAY FOR THE PEOPLE INTERVIEWING HER TO KNOW HOW MUCH

OF WHAT MOTHER SAID WAS REALITY AND HOW MUCH WAS ILLUSION. ANYWAY, SHE LOOKED LOVELY AND BEHAVED PERFECTLY AND WE GOT THE OK FOR HER TO MOVE IN.

AFTER THE INTERVIEW, WE WENT SHOPPING FOR NEW SUMMER-WEIGHT CLOTHES. SHE LOVED THE SHOPPING BUT LATER WHEN THOSE CLOTHES WERE HANGING IN HER NEW APARTMENT IN THE NEW CLOSET, SHE NEVER COULD FIGURE OUT THAT THEY WERE HER CLOTHES. SHE OFTEN CALLED ME TO ASK ME WHOSE CLOTHES WERE IN HER CLOSET. SOMETIMES, FOR WHATEVER REASON, SHE WOULD THINK THE APARTMENT BELONGED TO HER FRIEND GEORGINE. MOTHER WOULD ASK WHY GEORGINE HAD LEFT ALL THE CLOTHES IN THE CLOSET AND TELL ME THERE WAS NO ROOM FOR HER OWN CLOTHES. THEN SHE WOULD ACCUSE GEORGINE OF NOT LEAVING ANY FOOD FOR HER IN THE REFRIGERATOR, WHICH MOTHER DID NOT THINK WAS VERY HOSPITABLE. OTHER TIMES MOTHER WONDERED WHY MY CLOTHES WERE IN THE CLOSET OR WHY SHE WAS IN MY APARTMENT. SHE NEVER ACCEPTED THE FACT THAT THIS WAS HER APARTMENT WITH HER CLOTHES, NO MATTER HOW MANY TIMES WE HAD THE CONVERSATION.

THE NIGHT OF THE INTERVIEW AT THE ASSISTED LIVING FACILITY, MARGIE, MOTHER AND I WERE HAVING DINNER. SEVERAL TIMES MOTHER ASKED ME IF I WOULD LIKE TO LIVE IN FLORIDA AND SAID SHE WOULD NOT. I WAS GRATEFUL FOR MARGIE'S BEING THERE AND HEARING ALL OF THIS AS MARGIE THEN REALIZED HOW LITTLE NEW IMPUT MOTHER WAS RETAINING. THIS CONVERSATION WAS REPEATED AS LONG AS WE WERE VISITING MARGIE AND CONTINUED UNTIL WE MADE THE ACTUAL MOVE TO FLORIDA.

THE LAST NIGHT BEFORE WE LEFT MARGIE'S, MOTHER COULD NOT FIND HER NIGHTGOWN. THIS WAS NOT UNUSUAL AS SHE WAS MISPLACING THINGS REGULARLY BY THEN, AND SHE WAS IN A PLACE THAT WAS NOT HERS. WE SEARCHED EVERYWHERE. WE COULD NOT FIND IT IN THE HOUSE THAT ADDED FURTHER TO MOTHER'S DISORIENTATION. MARGIE FINALLY GAVE HER A NIGHTGOWN TO USE. THE NEXT MORNING MARGIE FOUND MOTHER'S NIGHTGOWN HANGING IN MARGIE'S CLOSET, ALL THE WAY ON THE OTHER SIDE OF THE HOUSE. WHY MY MOTHER PUT IT THERE IS A MYSTERY. IT JUST REINFORCED THAT MOTHER NEEDED TO BE IN A FACILITY WHERE SHE WOULD BE LOOKED AFTER AND WHERE SHE WOULD BE SAFE.

THE LOGISTICS OF MOVING HER, AND MOVING ME, AS I HAD DECIDED

TO MOVE TO FLORIDA FULL TIME WITH MOTHER, WERE BEYOND AWFUL. TALK ABOUT STRESS! THERE WAS NO GOOD WAY TO DO IT. I HAD A LARGE HOUSE TO SELL, MOTHER'S CONDO TO SELL, A HOUSE TO BUY IN FLORIDA, AND AN APARTMENT TO GET READY FOR MOTHER IN FLORIDA. MY FRIEND BARBARA CAME TO FLORIDA WITH ME A COUPLE OF WEEKS BEFORE I WAS GOING TO MOVE MOTHER INTO HER APARTMENT. BARBARA IS A WONDERFUL DECORATIVE PAINTER AND SHE PAINTED THE WALLS OF THE APARTMENT SO THAT THE APARTMENT WOULD RESEMBLE MOTHER'S CONDO AND SET OFF HER FURNITURE. I WAS TRYING TO MAKE IT AS MUCH LIKE THE HOME MOTHER WAS LEAVING AS I COULD. I WANTED IT TO FEEL FAMILIAR TO HER.

WHEN I WENT BACK TO CLEVELAND I HIRED A SERVICE TO SELL WHATEVER FURNITURE AND ACCESSORIES OF MOTHER'S AND MINE THAT WERE NOT GOING TO FLORIDA. I HAD SELF- IMPOSED DEADLINES, AND I WANTED TO GET MOTHER MOVED AS SOON AS I COULD SO THAT I COULD STOP WORRYING 24 HOURS A DAY. I DEFINITELY KNEW THAT SHE NEEDED SOME CARE AND THAT I COULD NOT PROVIDE IT.

SINCE OUR FURNITURE WAS COMING IN ONE TRUCK, RATHER THAN SHIPPING MOTHER'S FURNITURE BEFORE MINE WAS SHIPPED, I NEEDED SOME TEMPORARY FURNITURE FOR HER APARTMENT IN FLORIDA. I SCHEDULED MOTHER'S MOVE INTO HER FLORIDA APARTMENT TO TAKE PLACE TWO WEEKS BEFORE I WOULD BE MOVING INTO MY NEW HOUSE THERE. THIS MEANT SHE WOULD BE IN THIS NEW ENVIRONMENT WITHOUT HER FURNITURE FROM CLEVELAND. THE FACT THAT IT WAS UNFAMILAR FURNITURE WAS NOT A GOOD THING. SHE DID NOT EVEN LIKE THE FURNITURE VERY MUCH, WHICH MADE EVERYTHING WORSE. SHE HAD A BED AND A SOFA AND COULD FUNCTION. I GOT HER SETTLED IN AS BEST I COULD. NOWHERE ALONG THE LINE DID SHE ARGUE WITH ME ABOUT ANY OF THIS. I'M NOT AT ALL SURE SHE EVEN UNDERSTOOD WHAT WAS HAPPENING. HER NOT PROTESTING OR AGRUING WITH ME MADE IT EASIER TO GET IT DONE BUT IT ALSO MADE ME REALIZE HOW MUCH OF MY MOTHER WAS NO LONGER THERE. SHE WAS A FIERCELY INDEPENDENT WOMAN BEFORE THIS DISEASE SET IN AND NOW SHE WAS BEING PASSIVE ABOUT MAJOR DECISIONS IN HER LIFE.

WHEN WE WERE STILL IN CLEVELAND MY BEST FRIEND SINCE 6TH GRADE, KAREN, CAME TO MOTHER'S CONDO WITH ME AND HELPED ME GO THROUGH MOTHER'S CLOTHES, JEWELRY AND PERSONAL ITEMS WITH

MOTHER. THE THREE OF US DECIDED WHAT TO TAKE TO FLORIDA. HAVING KAREN WITH ME WAS A HUGE HELP. SHE AND MOTHER HAD KNOWN EACH OTHER FOR SO LONG. KAREN IS FAMILY FROM THAT POINT OF VIEW, AND MOTHER WAS NOT GOING TO FIGHT WITH KAREN, AND KAREN WAS NOT GOING TO BE IMPATIENT WITH MOTHER. SOMEHOW IT ALL GOT DONE, EVEN WITHOUT MOTHER REALLY COMPREHENDING MOST OF WHAT WE WERE DOING OR WHY WE WERE DOING IT.

MOTHER MOVED INTO THE ASSISTED LIVING APARTMENT WITHOUT MANY OF HER THINGS, AND SHE WAS NOT HAPPY. SHE WAS VERY CONFUSED. SHE HAD ONE BEAUTIFUL ORIENTAL PORCELAIN LAMP THAT HAD BELONGED TO HER PARENTS. I HAND CARRIED IT WITH US ON THE PLANE TO FLORIDA. WHEN I PUT IT IN HER NEW APARTMENT, SHE TOLD ME TO TAKE IT OUT OF THE APARTMENT. SHE SAID SHE DID NOT WANT IT TO BREAK THERE. THIS IS THE SAME LAMP I HAD WANTED FOR YEARS THAT SHE WOULD NOT LET ME HAVE. I NOW HAVE IT IN MY ENTRANCE ON TOP OF A CONSOLE THAT CAME FROM MY PARENTS' HOME. IT'S A REASSURING WAY TO ENTER THE HOUSE NOW BUT AT THE TIME I WAS VERY SAD THAT MOTHER WAS PARTING WITH THIS LAMP. IT SIGNALED TO ME THAT WE WERE ENTERING UNEXPLORED TERRITORY.

MOTHER OFTEN THOUGHT THAT THE ASSISTED LIVING FACILITY WAS A HOTEL AND WONDERED WHY THEY DID NOT MAKE UP THE BED DAILY. I COULD NOT CONVINCE HER THAT SHE WAS NOT STAYING IN A FIVE STAR HOTEL, BUT THAT INSTEAD THIS APARTMENT WAS HER NEW HOME. SHE WAS CONFUSED ABOUT WHY THERE WAS NOT MUCH FOOD IN THE REFRIGERATOR. THE FACILITY PROVIDED ALL THREE MEALS IN THE DINING ROOM ON THE FIRST FLOOR. MOTHER WAS NOT SURE HOW TO GET TO THE DINING ROOM, AGAIN AND AGAIN, ALTHOUGH SHE GOT THERE ON HER OWN EVERY DAY FOR ALL THREE MEALS. SHE JUST DID NOT REMEMBER THAT SHE WENT TO THE DINING ROOM. WHILE I WAS STILL IN CLEVELAND PACKING UP HER CONDO THINGS AND MY HOUSE THINGS, SHE WOULD CALL AND ASK WHERE SHE WAS SUPPOSED TO EAT. TO WRITE THAT SHE WAS UNHAPPY AND DEPRESSED AND CONFUSED THOSE FIRST TWO WEEKS IS A MAJOR UNDERSTATEMENT. THE FACT THAT I WAS IN CLEVELAND ONLY ADDED TO HER UNHAPPINESS, DEPRESSION AND CONFUSION. I HAD BECOME HER LIFE LINE AND I WAS NOT THERE FOR HER THOSE TWO WEEKS.

I COULD NOT PACK UP HER CONDO WITH HER IN THE CONDO, AND PACK UP MY HOUSE WITH HER TO WORRY ABOUT. SO I MADE THE BEST OF A BAD

DECISION BY MOVING HER BEFORE I COULD MOVE. I SPENT THE NEXT TWO WEEKS WORRYING ABOUT HER CONSTANTLY. SHE SPENT THE TIME BEING ANGRY, AND DEPRESSED – AND CALLING ME ALL THE TIME TO COMPLAIN ABOUT EVERYTHING. I HAVE LEARNED THAT I CANNOT BE IN TWO PLACES AT ONCE, AS OBVIOUS AS THAT APPEARS. I TRY HARD AND I WANTED HER TO BE HAPPY BUT I COULD NOT MAKE THIS HAPPEN ANY EASIER. EVEN OVER TWO YEARS LATER WHEN I RETHINK THIS SITUATION, I CANNOT COME UP WITH A BETTER OR EASIER WAY I COULD HAVE DONE THIS MOVE FOR BOTH OF US.

THE STAFF OF THE FACILITY TOLD ME THAT NO MATTER THE CIRCUMSTANCES, THE FIRST TWO WEEKS TO TWO MONTHS WERE THE HARDEST ADJUSTMENT. I EXPECT THAT THIS IS TRUE. THE FACT THAT SHE HAD TO TRAVEL ON HER OWN IN THE FACILITY WAS VERY DIFFICULT. MOTHER AND I HAD TRAVELED TOGETHER TO FAR CORNERS OF THE WORLD, BUT THIS WAS OUR FIRST TRIP TO THE LAND OF ALZHEIMER'S AND WE WERE NOT ALWAYS SURE OF THE BEST ROAD TO TAKE.

MOTHER HAD ONE FRIEND WHO LIVES IN MIAMI MOST OF THE YEAR. SHE WAS ONE OF THE FEW FRIENDS WHO HAD NOT DESERTED MOTHER TOTALLY. ONE DAY THIS FRIEND CALLED ME YELLING AT ME AND TELLING ME WHAT AN AWFUL DAUGHTER I WAS TO MOVE MOTHER TO AN ASSISTED LIVING FACILITY. SHE COULD NOT COMPREHEND HOW I COULD LEAVE MOTHER ALONE AT THE ASSISTED LIVING FACILITY. KEEP IN MIND THAT THIS FRIEND HAD NOT SEEN MOTHER FOR MONTHS AND HAD JUST A FEW SHORT TELEPHONE CALLS WITH HER. INSTEAD OF REACTING TO HER INSULTS, AS THAT IS WHAT THEY WERE, I ASKED HER IF SHE WOULD BE KIND ENOUGH TO DRIVE UP TO THE FACILITYAND VISIT WITH MOTHER WHILE I WAS STILL IN CLEVELAND TRYING TO GET EVERYTHING READY FOR MY MOVE. SHE BACKED DOWN ENOUGH THEN TO SAY SHE WOULD, AND SHE DID. PERHAPS THAT IS HOW MOTHER CONNECTED THE APARTMENT TO HER FRIEND GEORGINE. FOR THE ENTIRE STAY MOTHER OFTEN THOUGHT THAT THE APARTMENT WAS GEORGINE'S.

THE REALITY WAS THAT I NEEDED TO BE THERE FOR MY MOTHER. WE BOTH MANAGED TO GET THROUGH THE TWO WEEKS WHILE SHE WAS THERE WITHOUT ME. IT WAS NOT AS IF SHE WERE ALONE. THERE WAS WONDERFUL STAFF AND OTHER TENANTS, SOME OF WHOM SHE ACTUALLY ENJOYED. THERE WERE LOTS OF ACTIVITIES, MANY OF WHICH SHE NEVER REALLY

PARTICIPATED IN. MOTHER WAS NEVER MUCH OF A JOINER SO THAT WAS NO SURPRISE. IT WAS FORTUNATE THAT SHE ENJOYED HER OWN COMPANY BUT AT THIS POINT IN HER LIFE I WAS CONVINCED THAT SHE NEEDED SOME COMPANIONSHIP AND INTERACTION WITH OTHERS. I WAS HOPING THAT HER DEPENDENCE ON ME WOULD LESSEN, ALLOWING ME SOME TIME FOR ME, AND THAT SHE COULD HAVE SOME FRIENDS IN THE FACILITY SO THAT SHE WOULD DO SOME OF THE ACTIVITIES AND ENJOY LIFE AS BEST SHE COULD.

CHAPTER TWELVE
SETTLING IN

THE FIRST WEEKS OF MY MOVING TO FLORIDA WERE BUSY ONES. I HAD A GARAGE FULL OF BOXES TO UNPACK. I HAD MOTHER'S THINGS TO ORGANIZE SO THAT HER APARTMENT WOULD SEEM LIKE HOME TO HER. I HAD MY THREE CATS FROM CLEVELAND ADJUSTING TO A NEW HOME AS WELL AS THE TWO KITTENS I HAD JUST GOTTEN. THESE TWO KITTENS WERE STRAYS THAT THE STAFF AT THE ASSISTED LIVING FACILITY HAD RESCUED AND I HAD AGREED TO TAKE THEM ONCE I MOVED INTO THE HOUSE. MAYBE I FELT THAT I COULD MOTHER THESE KITTENS WHILE I WAS MOTHERING MY OWN MOTHER. ALL OF MY SUPPORT SYSTEM AT THAT TIME WAS IN CLEVELAND. I THINK I WAS SO BUSY GETTING EVERYTHING DONE, INCLUDING RUNNING MY BUSINESS, THAT I JUST DID NOT TAKE THE TIME TO REALIZE HOW MUCH STRESS BOTH MOTHER AND I WERE UNDER, AND HOW MANY NEW THINGS WE HAD TO LEARN.

MOTHER NEVER REALLY ADJUSTED TO BEING IN FLORIDA AND NOT BEING IN HER BEAUTIFUL CONDO IN CLEVELAND. EVEN THOUGH SHE HAD A LOT OF HER THINGS, INCLUDING MOST OF HER ART PIECES, MANY OF WHICH WERE FROM OUR TRAVELS. IN THE APARTMENT, SHE DID NOT RECOGNIZE THEM AS HERS. SHE CONTINUED TO ASK ME WHY SHE WAS STAYING IN THIS HOTEL, OR WHY SHE WAS IN MY APARTMENT OR EVEN STRANGER WHY SHE WAS IN HER FRIEND GEORGINE'S APARTMENT. MANY DAYS I GOT A PHONE CALL FROM HER ASKING WHY THERE WAS NO FOOD IN THE APARTMENT AND WHAT SHE WAS SUPPOSED TO EAT. I HAD TO REMIND HER HOW TO GET TO THE DINING ROOM. SHE COULD NOT UNDERSTAND WHY THE HOTEL DID NOT HAVE ROOM SERVICE. PERHAPS IT MADE IT EASIER FOR HER TO THINK SHE WAS ON A TRIP IN A HOTEL. ACTUALLY THE FACILITY DID PROVIDE ROOM SERVICE IF NECESSARY, BUT I FELT STRONGLY THAT MOTHER NEEDED TO GET OUT OF HER APARTMENT ON A REGULAR BASIS AND SOCIALIZE. NO MATTER WHAT I SAID TO HELP HER THROUGH THE CONFUSION, IT DID NOT SEEM TO MATTER. NONE OF IT APPEARED TO REGISTER. SHE COULD NO LONGER TAKE IN NEW INFORMATION.

AT FIRST SHE COMPLAINED ABOUT THE FOOD AND THE OTHER RESIDENTS. SHE DID NOT LIKE HER COMPANIONS AT MEAL TIMES. HOWEVER, LUCKY FOR HER AND LUCKY FOR ME, SHE EVENTUALLY CONNECTED WITH A WOMAN AND THEY BECAME GOOD FRIENDS. ELLIE ALSO HAD SOME MEMORY LOSS BUT NOT QUITE AS MUCH AS MY MOTHER DID. ELLIE

HAD A LOT OF PEP AND ENTHUSIASM. SHE WANTED TO PARTICIPATE IN EVERYTHING AND ENJOY WHAT THE FACILITY HAD TO OFFER. SHE STARTED DRAGGING MOTHER TO THE MOVIES AND THE MUSIC EVENTS, ALL OF WHICH MOTHER ENJOYED, AND NONE OF WHICH SHE WOULD HAVE GONE TO ON HER OWN.

OFTEN AFTER THEY HAD BEEN TO A MOVIE, WHICH WAS JUST IN THE ATTACHED BUILDING ON THE OTHER SIDE OF THE COMPLEX, MOTHER WOULD CALL ME AND TELL ME SHE AND ELLIE HAD BEEN OUT TO DINNER AND TO THE MOVIES. SHE ALWAYS MADE IT SOUND AS IF THEY HAD TAKEN A CAR AND GONE OUTSIDE OF THE COMPLEX. SHE ALWAYS SAID, "DON'T ASK ME WHAT WE SAW. I DON'T REMEMBER, BUT IT WAS GOOD."

ONE DAY MY BEST FRIENDS FROM CLEVELAND WERE VISITING. MOTHER HAD BEEN LIVING AT THE ASSISTED LIVING FACILITY FOR ALMOST SEVEN MONTHS AT THIS POINT. I HAD TOLD HER WE WOULD PICK HER UP TO TAKE HER TO LUNCH AFTER HER MANICURE. I HAD TOLD THE FACILITY STAFF THAT I WAS TAKING HER TO LUNCH AND WOULD MEET HER AT THE BEAUTY SHOP. WHEN WE GOT THERE SHE WAS NOT AT THE BEAUTY SHOP. SHE WAS NOT ANYWHERE IN THE LOBBY AND SHE WAS NOT IN HER APARTMENT. I WAS GETTING VERY CONCERNED. WHILE IT WAS UNLIKELY THAT SHE WOULD WANDER OFF THE PREMISES, SHE COULD HAVE. FINALLY WE FOUND HER WANDERING IN THE PARKING LOT LOOKING FOR HER CAR. OF COURSE, SHE DID NOT HAVE A CAR ANYMORE AND HAD NOT FOR MANY MONTHS, EVEN BEFORE MOVING TO FLORIDA, SO IT HAD NOT OCCURRED TO ME THAT SHE WOULD BE IN THE PARKING LOT SEARCHING FOR HER CAR.

MOTHER NEVER UNDERSTOOD THAT SHE DID NOT HAVE A CAR. WHEN I WAS PICKING HER UP TO GO OUT OF THE FACILITY, SHE ALWAYS ASKED ME IF I WERE GOING TO PICK HER UP IN THE GARAGE OR UPSTAIRS. THIS WAS A THROW BACK TO WHEN SHE WAS IN THE CONDO. IF THE WEATHER WERE BAD I ALWAYS PICKED HER UP IN THE GARAGE. THERE WAS NO GARAGE AT THE ASSISTED LIVING FACILITY AND I ALWAYS PICKED HER UP AT THE SIDE DOOR SO THERE COULD BE NO CONFUSION. EVEN WITH TRYING TO MAKE THAT A PATTERN, MOTHER WOULD SOMETIMES BE AT THE FRONT DOOR, AND I WOULD HAVE TO GO SEARCHING FOR HER. IT DID NOT CAUSE HER ANY PROBLEMS BUT IT CERTAINLY DID MAKE ME CRAZY AND STRESSED. I KNOW I ALSO WAS TRYING TO MAKE THINGS EASIER FOR MYSELF. I DID NOT WANT TO PARK AND GO UP TO HER APARTMENT TO GET HER. MY HAVING TO GO UP TO HER APARTMENT WOULD HAVE BEEN

ADMITTING THAT SHE WAS WORSE THAN EVEN I WANTED TO ACCEPT. WHENEVER I WOULD PICK MOTHER UP, SHE ALWAYS HAD A BOOK IN HER HANDS. THIS, AT LEAST, WAS REASSURING AS I HAD NEVER KNOWN MY MOTHER WITHOUT BOOKS. SHE ALWAYS WAS READING AND SHE INSTILLED IN ME A LOVE OF BOOKS. WE WOULD OFTEN COMPARE OUR THOUGHTS ON VARIOUS NOVELS, AND IT WAS SOMETHING WE SHARED. I RECENTLY READ A BOOK THAT MENTIONED THAT IF YOU HAD A BOOK YOU COULD TRAVEL ANYWHERE THROUGH THE BOOK. THIS REMINDED ME OF MY MOTHER. SHE ALWAYS SAID IF YOU HAD A BOOK, YOU WOULD NEVER BE LONELY. BOOKS WERE HER FRIENDS.

IN THE HALL OUTSIDE OF HER APARTMENT WAS A BOOKCASE FILLED WITH BOOKS ANY OF THE TENANTS COULD READ. THERE WAS ALSO A LARGE LIBRARY WITH CURRENT NOVELS, MAGAZINES AND NEWSPAPERS IN THE MAIN BUILDING. THIS ALWAYS SEEMED TO AMAZE MOTHER, AND PLEASE HER. SOMETIMES I WOULD ASK HER WHAT SHE WAS READING. SHE ALWAYS HAD TO LOOK AT THE BOOK IN HER HANDS IN ORDER TO ANSWER ME. I KNEW SHE WAS NOT RETAINING ANY OF THE STORY LINES OF THESE BOOKS, BUT IT DID NOT SEEM TO MATTER TO HER, AND SO IT WAS NOT DISTURBING TO ME. IT WAS JUST ANOTHER REMINDER ABOUT MY HAVING TO LIVE IN HER WORLD, NOT HER HAVING TO LIVE IN MINE.

WHEN WE WERE STILL IN CLEVELAND, WE WOULD OFTEN GO TO HER COUNTRY CLUB FOR MEALS. IT WAS EASY, FAMILIAR, AND THE FOOD WAS QUITE GOOD. WHEN WE MOVED TO FLORIDA, I WOULD TAKE HER OUT, BUT NOWHERE WE WENT WAS FAMILIAR. INSTEAD OF THIS BEING AN ADVENTURE FOR HER, IT WAS ALARMING. THIS WAS A WOMAN WHO TRAVELED TO PRE-INDUSTRIAL CHINA AS SOON AS IT WAS OPEN TO TOURISTS, AND NOW SHE WAS AFRAID TO LEAVE THE ASSISTED LIVING FACILITY. WHEN I DID TAKE HER OUT SHE WOULD NOT BE CERTAIN WHAT TO ORDER, AND THEN SHE WOULD FORGET WHAT SHE HAD ORDERED, OR THAT SHE HAD ORDERED AT ALL. SHE LOST HER AWARENESS OF TIME IN THESE UNFAMILIAR RESTAURANTS. I STILL TRIED TO TAKE HER OUT, FOR MY SAKE AS MUCH AS FOR HERS I SUSPECT, EVEN THOUGH IT WAS HARD FOR BOTH OF US. I WANTED TO MAINTAIN SOME SEMBLANCE OF OUR OLD LIFE TOGETHER FOR AS LONG AS I COULD. I MISTAKENLY THOUGHT IT WOULD BE BETTER FOR HER, AND FOR ME.LOOKING BACK, I DO NOT THINK THIS WAS THE BEST THING TO DO. SHE WAS CONFUSED IN MY NEW HOUSE SO THAT WAS NOT THE SOLUTION. IT FINALLY WORKED BEST IF I ATE AT THE FACILITY WITH HER.

MOTHER WAS NOT EATING A LOT AND WAS LOSING SOME WEIGHT. AFTER CONSULTING WITH THE NURSING STAFF AT THE ASSISTED LIVING FACILITY, WE DECIDED TO TRY TO GET HER TO DRINK "ENSURE". MUCH TO MY SURPRISE, SHE DID NOT RESIST THIS AND ACTUALLY SAID SHE LIKED THE "ENSURE". WORRYING ABOUT HER PHYSICAL HEALTH WAS ALWAYS ON MY MIND AS I THOUGHT THAT SOMEHOW I COULD TAKE CARE OF THIS EVEN THOUGH I COULD NOT TAKE CARE OF HER MEMORY LOSS. IF I THOUGHT OF MYSELF AS THE TOUR DIRECTOR ON THIS JOURNEY, I KNEW I WANTED TO HAVE SOME OF THE PLACES WE WENT NOT BE RANDOM, BUT INSTEAD BE PLACES WE COULD COUNT ON AS WE HAD BEEN TO THEM BEFORE.

ONE THING THIS DISEASE REQUIRES FROM THE CAREGIVERS IS A HUGE AMOUNT OF PATIENCE. EVERYTHING TAKES LONGER. SOMEONE WITH ALZHEIMER'S SLOWS DOWN AND OFTEN DOES OR DOES NOT DO THINGS THAT MAKE A LOT OF SENSE TO THOSE OF US WATCHING THE PERSON. JUST TO GET THROUGH A MEAL REQUIRED MORE TIME. JUST TO HAVE MOTHER WALK DOWN THE HALL TO THE ELEVATOR TOOK MORE TIME. MOTHER WAS ALWAYS THE ONE WALKING AHEAD OF ME ON TRIPS OR WHEREVER WE WERE. NOW I HAD TO SLOW MYSELF DOWN - A LOT – SO THAT WE COULD WALK TOGETHER.

CHAPTER THIRTEEN
WONDERING IF WE HAVE PACKED THE RIGHT MEDICINES

MOTHER WAS ALWAYS ASKING ME WHO WOULD TAKE CARE OF ME WHEN I NEEDED THE CARE I WAS GIVING HER.

MOTHER HAD BEEN UNDER ONE DOCTOR'S CARE FOR SEVERAL YEARS BEFORE SHE WAS DIAGNOSED WITH ALZHEIMERS. SHORTLY AFTER THE DIAGNOSIS HE RETIRED TO DO ONLY RESEARCH. SINCE HE WAS ALSO MY DOCTOR I HAD TO FIND A DOCTOR FOR BOTH OF US. BY THIS TIME MOTHER WAS ON SEVERAL DIFFERENT MEDICINES, FOR A VARIETY OF AILMENTS INCLUDING BORDERLINE DIABETES. RECENTLY THERE WAS A STUDY FROM THE CENTER FOR BRAIN HEALTH AT NEW YORK UNIVERSITY LINKING IMPAIRED GLUCOSE TOLERANCE (INSULIN RESISTENCY) TO DIABETES AND IN TURN TO MEMORY LOSS. AT THE TIME MOTHER WAS FINALLY DIAGNOSED WITH DIABETES, SHE HAD ALZHEIMERS FOR A FEW YEARS AND THIS STUDY HAD NOT YET COME OUT. MOTHER'S HAVING DIABETES PERHAPS WAS SOMEHOW CONNECTED TO HER MEMORY LOSS. IT IS SO IMPORTANT TO STAY UPDATED CONSTANTLY ON CHANGING MEDICAL NEWS RELATING TO ALZHEIMER'S. THE GOOD NEWS IS THAT THERE IS MUCH RESEARCH BEING DONE AND NEW THINGS ABOUT THE DISEASE BEING LEARNED ALL THE TIME.

WE WERE STILL IN CLEVELAND AT THE TIME WHEN THIS DOCTOR RETIRED. I WAS ABLE TO FIND ANOTHER DOCTOR WHO COULD TREAT US BOTH. I HAVE ALWAYS LIKED BEING IN THE SAME OFFICE AS MY MOTHER SO THAT THE DOCTOR COULD TREAT THE FAMILY AND KNOW THE FAMILY HISTORY. OUR NEW DOCTOR CHANGED MOTHER'S MEDICINES SOME, BUT NOT MUCH. MOTHER WAS USED TO TAKING HER MEDICINES AS SHE HAD FOR THE PAST FEW YEARS. SHE WAS STILL LIVING ALONE AT THIS TIME. SHE DID NOT WANT ANY ASSISTANCE WITH HER MEDICINES, NO MATTER HOW MANY TIMES I SUGGESTED HAVING SOME HELP. I WAS CONCERNED THAT IF WE CHANGED HER MEDICINES, SHE WOULD NOT BE ABLE TO ACCEPT THE CHANGE AND TAKE HER MEDICINES PROPERLY.

THIS NEW DOCTOR ALSO SUGGESTED PUTTING MY MOTHER ON INSULIN, BUT THERE WOULD HAVE BEEN NO WAY MOTHER COULD HAVE GIVEN

HERSELF INSULIN AND NO WAY I COULD BE AT HER APARTMENT EVERY DAY TO GIVE HER INSULIN. THE DOCTOR AND I DECIDED, AS WE KNEW BY THEN THAT MOTHER AND I WERE MOVING TO FLORIDA, TO WAIT. WHEN WE GOT TO FL AND MOTHER WAS IN THE ASSISTED LIVING FACILITY THE NURSING STAFF THERE COULD MONITOR THE INSULIN.

AGAIN, IN FLORIDA, I HAD TO FIND DOCTORS FOR BOTH OF US. FINDING A DOCTOR IN A NEW CITY IS NOT THE EASIEST THING TO DO. THE ASSISTED LIVING FACILITY SUGGESTED I CALL THE CLOSEST HOSPITAL AS THE HOSPITAL HAD A REFERRAL SYSTEM. KEEP IN MIND THAT I WAS MOVING US TO SOUTH FLORIDA. I CALLED THE REFERRAL SYSTEM AT THE HOSPITAL AND TOLD THE WOMAN ON THE PHONE THAT I NEEDED A DOCTOR FOR MY MOTHER WHO SPECIALIZED IN GERIATICS AND A DOCTOR FOR ME WHO SPECIALIZED IN WOMEN'S HEALTH. AFTER THIS LONG REQUEST, THE WOMAN AT THE REFERRAL SYSTEM GAVE ME ANOTHER NUMBER TO CALL.

IT TURNED OUT TO BE AN 800 NUMBER IN MIAMI. I WENT THROUGH THE SAME REQUESTS AGAIN AND THIS WOMAN WHO HAD A HEAVY SPANISH ACCENT SAID SHE WOULD BE HAPPY TO HELP ME. SHE STARTED GIVING ME NAMES OF DOCTORS, TELLING ME THE DOCTORS' SCHOOL BACKGROUNDS, THEIR EXPERIENCE, ETC. BUT ALL THE DOCTORS SHE GAVE ME HAD SPANISH SOUNDING NAMES. I TOLD HER THAT SHE SHOULD NOT TAKE WHAT I WAS ABOUT TO SAY THE WRONG WAY. MOTHER WAS JEWISH AND HAD ALWAYS GONE TO JEWISH DOCTORS. I ASKED HER TO TRY TO FIND SOME JEWISH DOCTORS ON HER LIST. SHE SAID, " I WILL BE HAPPY TO GIVE YOU JEWISH DOCTORS, BUT I DON'T KNOW JEWISH NAMES." WELCOME TO SOUTH FLORIDA!

EVENTUALLY I GOT THE NAMES OF SERVERAL DOCTORS AND WAS ABLE TO CALL FOR APPOINTMENTS. IT WAS REQUIRED BY THE ASSISTED LIVING FACILITY THAT MOTHER HAVE A DOCTOR BEFORE SHE COULD MOVE INTO THE FACILITY. I HAD WANTED TO INTERVIEW THE DOCTORS BEFORE MAKING A DECISION, BUT THE FIRST OFFICE I CALLED SAID THAT THE DOCTOR HAD SEVERAL PATIENTS AT THE ASSISTED LIVING FACILITY, AND THAT WAS GOOD ENOUGH FOR ME. I MADE AN APPOINTMENT FOR THE DOCTOR TO SEE MY MOTHER AFTER WE BOTH HAD MOVED TO FLORIDA.

MOTHER'S DOCTOR WAS A SPECIALIST IN GERIATICS. SHE TOTALLY CHANGED ALL MY MOTHER'S MEDICINES. IT WAS EASY TO DO AT THIS TIME AS THE STAFF AT THE ASSISTED LIVING FACILITY WOULD GIVE MOTHER

HER MEDICINES AT EACH MEAL. THE PHARMACY WOULD, ON A MONTHLY BASIS, SEND THE MEDICINES PACKED FOR EACH MEAL AND EACH DAY TO THE ASSISTED LIVING FACILITY. THIS WAS SUCH A RELIEF TO ME. I KNEW SHE WOULD BE CARED FOR PROPERLY AND THAT THERE WOULD NOT BE DAYS WHEN SHE TOOK TOO MUCH OR TOO LITTLE MEDICINE.

ONE OF THE LESSONS IN THIS EXPERIENCE WAS THAT I SHOULD HAVE INTERVENED IN HER MEDICINE TAKING EARLIER, AS DIFFICULT AS THAT WOULD HAVE BEEN. I THINK MANY DOCTORS HAVE A TENDENCY TO KEEP A PATIENT ON THE SAME MEDICINES THEY HAVE BEEN ON FOR YEARS AS LONG AS THE PATIENT APPEARS TO BE HEALTHY ON THIS REGIMEN. THEY SELDOM ANALYZE WHY THE PATIENT WAS PUT ON THE MEDICINE IN THE FIRST PLACE, AND IF IT STILL MAKES SENSE FOR THE PATIENT TO CONTINUE ON THE MEDICINE YEARS LATER. I HAVE BECOME AN ADVOCATE OF GERIATIC DOCTORS FOR THIS REASON. THEY LOOK AT THE TOTAL PATIENT, THEIR CIRCUMSTANCES AND THEIR LIFE STYLE, THEIR PHYSICAL AND MENTAL HEALTH. THEY USE THE NEWEST MAPS FOR THE TRIP RATHER THAN MAPS THAT ARE NO LONGER CURRENT.

AFTER THE FIRST MONTH OF BEING ON THIS NEW MEDICINE REGIMEN, I ACTUALLY NOTICED AN IMPROVEMENT IN MOTHER'S HEALTH. I TOOK HER TO ALL HER DOCTOR APPOINTMENTS AND HER BLOOD PRESSURE, WHICH HAD BEEN HIGH FOR YEARS, WAS NOW NORMAL. MANY OF HER OTHER AILMENTS HAD IMPROVED. I WAS DELIGHTED. I THINK SOMETIMES MEDICINES JUST KEEP BEING GIVEN TO OLDER PATIENTS WITHOUT REAL CONCERN ABOUT THE INTERACTION OF THE MEDICINES OR WHETHER THEY ARE NECESSARY.

DOCTORS DON'T ALWAYS HAVE THE PATIENCE FOR SOMEONE WITH ALZHEIMERS. AS AN ADVOCATE FOR YOUR LOVED ONE, YOU MUST INSIST THAT EXTRA TIME BE ALLOTTED FOR THEIR APPOINTMENTS IN AN ATTEMPT TO TREAT THE PATIENT WITH DIGNITY.

I WOULD TAKE MOTHER TO THE DENTIST FOR HER CHECK UPS AND CLEANINGS, AT FIRST TRYING TO COMBINE MY TIMES WITH HERS. AFTER DOING THIS ONCE, I DECIDED IT WOULD BE BETTER IF I JUST TOOK HER TO HER APPOINTMENT AND MADE MINE FOR ANOTHER TIME. I WAS TOO CONCERNED ABOUT HER SITTING BY HERSELF IN THE WAITING ROOM. A GOOD PART OF MY WORRYING WAS SELF- IMPOSED. I WOULD SOMETIMES MAKE DECISIONS BASED ON NOT WANTING TO TAKE EXTRA TIME OR BEING

INCONVENIENCED. THOSE WERE ALMOST ALWAYS THE WRONG DECISIONS. AFTER MOTHER DIED, THE DENTIST'S RECEPTIONIST CALLED TO REMIND ME OF AN APPOINTMENT COMING UP FOR MY MOTHER. THE DENTIST'S OFFICE HAD NO WAY OF KNOWING MOTHER HAD DIED. THOSE KINDS OF MOMENTS WERE, AND CONTINUE TO BE, HARD. THEY SNEAK UP ON YOU AND CATCH YOU UNAWARE. AS I WAS GETTING MY TEETH CLEANED THE OTHER DAY I THOUGHT OF THIS CALL AND OF HOW MUCH I STILL MISS MY MOTHER.

I HAVE BEEN CONCERNED ABOUT THIS DISEASE BEING GENETIC AND OF MY GETTING IT EVENTUALLY. I HAVE VERY LITTLE FAMILY HISTORY AS MY GRANDFATHERS HAD DIED BEFORE I WAS BORN AND BOTH MY GRANDMOTHERS DIED WHEN I WAS QUITE YOUNG. THE FIRST TIME I SAW MY INTERNIST AFTER MOTHER DIED, SHE SAID TO ME THAT THE KIND OF ALZHEIMERS MY MOTHER HAD WAS NOT GENETIC AND THAT I SHOULD NOT WORRY ABOUT MY GETTING IT. I DON'T KNOWWHY SHE SAID THIS, OR IF SHE REALLY KNEW FOR SURE THAT WHAT SHE WAS SAYING WAS TRUE. I DO KNOW THAT EVERYONE I KNOW WHO HAS HAD A LOVED ONE WITH ALZHEIMERS WORRIES ABOUT GETTING IT THEMSELVES. MY MOTHER ALWAYS WAS ASKING ME WHO WOULD TAKE CARE OF ME WHEN I NEEDED THE KIND OF CARE I WAS GIVING HER.

WE HAD TAKEN OUT A LONG TERM CARE POLICY FOR MOTHER SHORTLY AFTER MY FATHER PASSED AWAY. WHILE IT NEVER WENT INTO EFFECT IN THE ASSISTED LIVING FACILITY, I KNEW THAT IT WAS THERE AS A SAFETY NET. ASSISTED LIVING FACILITIES AND NURSING HOMES CAN BE EXPENSIVE.

CHAPTER FOURTEEN
OUR ITINERARY

IT WAS ONLY WHEN I WAS NO LONGER CARING FOR MY MOTHER THAT I REALIZED I HAD BEEN IN A TORNADO FOR MONTHS AND LIFTED OFF THE GROUND OF REALITY.

LIFE IN FLORIDA SETTLED DOWN TO A ROUTINE. I WOULD STOP BY TO SEE MOTHER AT LEAST ONCE A DAY, AND SOMETIMES TWICE. IF I STOPPED BY IN THE AFTERNOON I WOULD ALWAYS TAKE ONE OF THE COOKIES FROM THE BAR AREA.THE COOKIES WERE MADE IN THE FACILITY AND WERE DELICIOUS. I WOULD EAT THE COOKIE ON MY WAY UP TO MOTHER'S APARTMENT. THIS WAS MY STRESS RELIEVER. I GAINED TEN POUNDS IN THE FIRST FEW MONTHS; I STOPPED EATING THE COOKIES. I LIKED TO VARY THE ROUTINE SO THAT THE STAFF DID NOT KNOW WHEN I WAS COMING. IT NEVER MATTERED AT THIS FACILITY. THE STAFF WAS ALWAYS ATTENTIVE AND FRIENDLY AND DOING THEIR JOB.

A GOOD DEAL OF MY LIFE REVOLVED AROUND MY MOTHER IN THOSE MONTHS. WHEN I WAS NOT WITH HER, SHE WAS OFTEN CALLING ME TO SEE WHERE I WAS. SOMETIMES THERE COULD BE DOZENS OF PHONE CALLS IN A DAY. OFTEN THEY WOULD BE REPEAT CONVERSATIONS. I WAS ALWAYS WORRYING ABOUT HER, EVEN THOUGH I KNEW THAT SHE WAS BEING CARED FOR 24 HOURS SEVEN DAYS A WEEK.

THERE WERE DAYS WHEN I PRAYED FOR THE PHONE NOT TO RING. IT WAS AN EXHAUSTING EXPERIENCE FOR ME. I RECENTLY WAS GOING THROUGH ALL THE CARDS AND LETTERS I RECEIVED FROM PEOPLE AFTER MOTHER DIED. ONE OF THEM STARTED WITH "NOW THAT YOUR MOTHER HAS FOUND HER PEACE, I TRUST THAT YOUR LIFE WILL GET BACK TO A MORE NORMAL PACE." IT WAS ONLY WHEN I WAS NO LONGER CARING FOR MY MOTHER THAT I REALIZED I HAD BEEN IN A TORNADO FOR MONTHS, AND LIFTED OFF THE GROUND OF REALITY. MOTHER WAS MY REALITY ALL THOSE MONTHS. ONLY AFTER SHE DIED DID I RECOGNIZE THAT I HAD GOTTEN OUT OF MY REALITY.

CHAPTER FIFTEEN
NEAR THE END OF THE JOURNEY

MOTHER AND I HAD MOVED TO FLORIDA IN MAY. BY THANKSGIVING MOTHER HAD BECOME VERY LETHARGIC. SHE HAD LOST WEIGHT AND SHE WAS NOW TAKING 'ENSURE" DAILY IN AN EFFORT TO PUT ON SOME OF THE LOST WEIGHT. SHE SEEMED MORE CONFUSED. THANKSGIVING WAS AT MY HOUSE, AND MOST OF THE FRIENDS AT DINNER WERE NEW FRIENDS. WHILE ONCE THIS WOULD HAVE BEEN EXCITING TO MOTHER, NOW IT WAS FRIGHTENING.SHE JUST WANDERED AROUND THE HOUSE SEEMINGLY LOST. OF COURSE, SHE WAS. SHE WAS NEVER REALLY COMFORTABLE IN MY FLORIDA HOUSE. SOME OF HER FURNITURE FROM HER CLEVELAND CONDO WAS IN MY HOUSE, BUT SHE NEVER SEEMED TO RECOGNIZE ANY OF THE PIECES.

THE DAY AFTER CHRISTMAS MOTHER AND I WENT TO LUNCH AT THE PLAZA ACROSS THE STREET FROM HER APARTMENT WITH MARGIE AND ROZ AND JERRY. MOTHER HAD KNOWN ROZ AND JERRY FOR MANY YEARS, AS ROZ IS MARGIE'S SISTER-IN-LAW. MARGIE'S HUSBAND BEN HAD BEEN GONE FOR OVER FIFTEEN YEARS AT THIS TIME. WHEN MOTHER AND I WERE WALKING INTO THE RESTAURANT MOTHER ASKED IF BEN, MARGIE'S HUSBAND, WOULD BE THERE TOO. NO MATTER HOW MANY TIMES THIS KIND OF THING HAPPENED, IT WAS ALWAYS DISCONCERTING.

IT WAS A COLD DAY FOR FLORIDA, OVERCAST WITH A REAL CHILL IN THE AIR. MOTHER WAS SHUFFLING RATHER THAN WALKING THAT DAY. WHILE HER WALKING PACE HAD SLOWED DOWN OVER THE PAST FEW YEARS, THIS DAY SHE WALKED EVEN MORE SLOWLY. BOTH MARGIE AND I COMMENTED ON MOTHER'S SHUFFLING, BUT DID NOT THINK IT WAS CAUSE FOR REAL CONCERN.

CHAPTER SIXTEEN
THE END OF THE JOURNEY

I FELT LIKE A STRANGER STRANDED ON AN ISLAND, AND THIS MAN FROM HOSPICE WAS RESCUING ME.

THE NEXT DAY I HAD A CALL FROM THE NURSE ON DUTY AT THE ASSISTED LIVING FACILITY SAYING THAT SHE DID NOT THINK MY MOTHER WAS QUITE RIGHT. MOTHER HAD NOT GONE DOWN FOR BREAKFAST THAT MORNING, SO THE NURSE HAD GONE UPSTAIRS TO LOOK FOR HER. THE NURSE TOLD ME THAT MOTHER HAD BEEN IN HER NIGHTGOWN AND DID NOT SEEM TO KNOW HOW TO GET DRESSED. SHE WENT ON TO SAY THAT MOTHER USED TO ALWAYS LOOK HER IN THE EYE, BUT THIS MORNING SHE WAS HANGING HER HEAD AND AVOIDING DOING SO. THE NURSE CALLED THE DOCTOR AND THEN CALLED ME.

THIS WAS THE SECOND DAY AFTER CHRISTMAS. OUR DOCTOR WAS ON VACATION. THE DOCTOR ON CALL FOR THE PRACTICE TOLD THE NURSE TO CALL AN AMBULANCE AND GET MOTHER TO THE EMERGENCY ROOM. BY THE TIME I GOT THE CALL, MOTHER WAS ALREADY AT THE HOSPITAL.

WHEN I GOT TO THE EMERGENCY ROOM, MOTHER WAS ON A COT, IN CLOTHES THAT SHE HAD OBVIOUSLY SOILED FROM THE SMELL. SHE WAS WITHOUT HER GLASSES, AND YET SHE APPEARED TO BE VERY CONTENT. I DO NOT THINK SHE HAD ANY IDEA WHERE SHE WAS OR WHY. I, HOWEVER, FELT THAT WE WERE IN A STRANGE LAND, ONE I DID NOT WANT TO BE IN. AT THE TIME I NOTICED SHE HAD A BRUISE ON HER FOREHEAD. WHEN I GOT TO HER APARTMENT THE NEXT DAY TO GET HER GLASSES AND SOME THINGS LIKE PHOTOS TO PUT BY HER BEDSIDE, I FOUND THE GLASSES ON THE FLOOR AND THE WASTEPAPER BASKET IN THE BEDROOM OVERTURNED. WHAT I THINK HAPPENED IS THAT SHE HAD A STROKE AND FELL. THE NURSE SAID SHE HAD FOUND MOTHER ON THE FLOOR WHEN SHE HAD COME UP TO THE APARTMENT THE DAY BEFORE.

THE EMERGENCY ROOM WAS IN THE NORMAL CHAOS OF AN EMERGENCY ROOM. THEY DID NOT HAVE A ROOM FOR MOTHER, AND THEN HAD ONE WITHOUT SOME KIND OF MONITOR THAT THEY WANTED TO HAVE HER ON. THEY HAD ADMITTED HER WITH PNEUMOMIA, WHICH STILL PUZZLES

ME. SHE HAD NO COUGH, NO SHORTNESS OF BREATH AND NO SYMPTOMS OF PNEUMONIA THAT WERE VISIBLE TO ME. I INSISTED THAT THEY CALL THE DOCTOR TO GET PERMISSION TO PUT HER IN THE AVAILABLE ROOM WITHOUT THE MONITOR, JUST TO GET HER IN A ROOM. FINALLY THEY MOVED HER UPSTAIRS.

I NO LONGER REMEMBER IF SHE WAS IN A PRIVATE ROOM OR HAD A ROOMMATE. EVERY TIME I WENT TO THE HOSPITAL DURING THE NEXT FEW DAYS THE SITUATION CHANGED. MARGIE AND I WERE THERE ONE DAY AROUND LUNCH TIME AND WHILE I HELPED MOTHER TO EAT HER SANDWICH, SHE KEEP ASKING WHAT WE WERE GOING TO DO THAT DAY. IT WAS AS IF SHE THOUGHT WE WERE GOING TO GO SHOPPING OR TO A MUSEUM. SHE WAS DEFINITELY IN HER OWN WORLD, WHICH WAS GOOD AS SHE WAS MOSTLY CONTENT.

THAT NIGHT I GOT A CALL FROM THE NURSING STAFF ASKING ME TO COME TO THE HOSPITAL. MOTHER WAS AGITATED AND WAS TRYING TO PULL OUT HER IV AND OXYGEN. IT WAS VERY LATE IN THE EVENING WHEN I GOT THIS CALL. I ASKED THE NURSE WHAT SHE THOUGHT MY BEING THERE WOULD ACCOMPLISH. SHE SAID MAYBE I COULD CALM MOTHER DOWN. I NEXT ASKED WHAT WOULD HAPPEN IF AS SOON AS I LEFT SHE GOT AGITATED AGAIN. THE NURSE SAID SHE WOULD HAVE TO PUT RESTRAINTS ON MOTHER. I GAVE HER PERMISSION TO PUT ON THE RESTRAINTS THEN. I KNEW THAT I WOULD BE NO GOOD TO MOTHER THE NEXT DAY IF I DID NOT GET SOME SLEEP AND THAT MY RUNNING TO THE HOSPITAL WOULD BE A VERY TEMPORARY SOLUTION.

WHEN I SAW MOTHER THE FOLLOWING MORNING SHE WAS CALM AND WE ACTUALLY HAD SOME CONVERSATION. MOST OF IT HAD NO MEANING FROM AN ACTUAL TIME LINE, BUT BY THIS TIME I WAS ALMOST USED TO THAT KIND OF ALICE-IN-WONDERLAND CONVERSATION WITH HER. AT THIS POINT I AM SURE SHE HAD A ROOMMATE AS I REMEMBER MOTHER TALKING WITH THE ROOMMATE'S FAMILY. THIS WAS TOTALLY UNLIKE MY MOTHER. UNDER NORMAL CONDITIONS SHE WOULD HAVE HAD NO CONVERSATION WITH PEOPLE SHE DID NOT KNOW.

THE NEXT MORNING I WALKED IN AND SAW THERE WAS ONLY ONE BED IN THE ROOM. BEFORE I ACTUALLY SAW MOTHER, I SAID OUT LOUD, "OH, I GUESS YOU HAVE YOUR PRIVATE ROOM BACK". THEN I NOTICED THIS LARGE PIECE OF EQUIPMENT IN THE ROOM NEXT TO HER BED. IT WAS LIFE SUPPORT OXYGEN.

THE DAY AFTER MOTHER WAS ADMITTED INTO THE HOSPITAL I TOOK A COPY OF THE LIVING WILL AND MY POWER OF ATTORNEY TO THE HOSPITAL. MOTHER AND I HAD TALKED ABOUT THIS YEARS EARLIER AND AGREED THAT THERE SHOULD BE NO HEROICS AT THE END. THE DAY BEFORE I GOT TO THE HOSPITAL TO FIND MY MOTHER ON LIFE SUPPORT, THE DOCTOR ON CALL HAD ORDERED UP A TEST TO INSERT A LONG TUBE DOWN HER THROAT. FORTUNATELY THE HOSPITAL NEEDED MY PERMISSION TO DO THIS TEST. I DENIED PERMISSION AND WHEN I TALKED TO THE DOCTOR I TOLD HIM THAT MY MOTHER HAD ALZHEIMERS. I WAS NOT GOING TO ALLOW A TEST THAT COULD BE PAINFUL.

THIS WAS A BLATANT CASE OF A DOCTOR NOT AGREEING WITH THE END OF LIFE CHOICES MY MOTHER AND I HAD MADE FOR HER. THANKFULLY WE HAD ALL THE LEGAL PAPERS IN PLACE. THEY HAD ALL BEEN DONE IN CLEVELAND WITH OUR ATTORNEY THERE, AND I HAD JUST A FEW WEEKS EARLIER ASKED THE ATTORNEY TO DRAW UP NEW PAPERS WITH OUR FLORIDA ADDRESSES. THEY CAME A FEW DAYS AFTER MY MOTHER PASSED AWAY.

WHILE I WAS TALKING WITH THIS DOCTOR WHO WAS OVERSEEING MOTHER'S CASE, I WAS AT THE NURSES' STATION. A KIND MAN FROM HOSPICE WAS ALSO THERE AND OVERHEARD MY END OF THE PHONE CONVERSATION. I HAD ASKED THE DOCTOR TO GIVE THE ORDER TO TAKE OFF THE LIFE SUPPORT. HE FINALLY AGREED TO DO THIS AND SAID HE WOULD SIGN THE FORMS THE NEXT DAY. HE INSISTED ON KEEPING HER ON IV ANTIBIOTICS, HOWEVER, AS SHE HAD BEEN ADMITTED WITH PNEUMONIA. THIS MADE NO SENSE TO ME BUT I AGREED IN ORDER TO GET DONE WHAT NEEDED TO BE DONE. THE MAN FROM HOSPICE ASKED IF I NEEDED HELP. TRUTHFULLY, I HAD NO IDEA. I HAD NEVER BEEN IN THIS SITUATION BEFORE. I FELT LIKE A STRANGER STRANDED ON AN ISLAND, AND THIS MAN FROM HOSPICE WAS RESCUING ME.

HE EXPLAINED THAT SOMEONE FROM HOSPICE WOULD COME TO THE HOSPITAL AND BE THERE WITH ME AND MY FAMILY WHILE THE LIFE SUPPORT WAS REMOVED; THEY WOULD ALSO TAKE CARE OF THE PAPERWORK. I WAS SO THANKFUL FOR THE HELP. I CALLED MARGIE AND SHE AND HER SON-IN-LAW JERRY INSISTED ON BEING WITH ME AT THE HOSPITAL THE NEXT DAY.

I HAD NO IDEA WHAT TO EXPECT. JERRY HAD BEEN PRESENT WHEN LIFE

SUPPORT WAS TAKEN OFF FOR TWO OTHERS. HE TOLD ME NOT TO EXPECT INSTANT DEATH. THE HOSPICE WOMAN ALSO TOLD ME THAT. I HAD ALWAYS THOUGHT THAT ONCE LIFE SUPPORT WAS REMOVED THE PERSON WOULD JUST DIE. I WAS SO LUCKY TO HAVE CARING PEOPLE WITH ME DURING THIS EXPERIENCE.

ONE OF THE NURSES HAD NEVER DONE THIS PROCEDURE BEFORE AND SHE WAS OBVIOUSLY NERVOUS ABOUT IT. SHE KEPT TALKING TO MY MOTHER, RUBBING HER ARM AND TRYING TO KEEP MOTHER, AND HERSELF, CALM. THE DOCTOR WHO ACTUALLY TOOK OFF ALL THE LIFE SUPPORT TOLD ME THAT NOT EVEN FOR ONE MINUTE SHOULD I THINK THIS WAS THE WRONG DECISION. HER SAYING THAT HELPED A LOT. THE OXYGEN AND ANTIBIOTICS WERE REMOVED. ALL THAT REMAINED WAS AN IV WITH MORPHINE DRIP TO ASSURE THAT MOTHER WOULD NOT BE IN ANY PAIN. IT WAS INTERESTING THAT ALL THE PEOPLE IN THE ROOM BUT JERRY WERE WOMEN, AND THAT THEY WERE ALL SO KIND AND CARING. WHEN THEY LEFT US ALONE WITH MOTHER, THEY ALL GAVE ME HUGS.

IT MADE THE EXPERIENCE EVEN MORE EMOTIONAL BUT IT ALSO HELPED ME TO KNOW I HAD A SUPPORT SYSTEM, EVEN THOUGH IT WAS A SUPPORT SYSTEM OF STRANGERS.

THE WOMAN FROM HOSPICE HAD LEARNED FROM HER EXPERIENCE THAT IF THE PERSON WHO HAD JUST HAD THE LIFE SUPPORT REMOVED DID NOT EXPIRE WITHIN THE HOUR OF THE REMOVAL, IT WAS LIKELY THE PERSON WOULD HANG ON FOR QUITE SOME TIME. SHE PREFERRED KEEPING THE PERSON IN THE HOSPITAL ROOM FOR AN HOUR BEFORE MOVING THE PERSON TO THE HOSPICE WING. SHE DID NOT LIKE HAVING A PATIENT EXPIRE IN THE HALL AS SHE DID NOT THINK THAT WAS DIGNIFIED. SO WE WAITED THE HOUR. JERRY TAUGHT ME TO COUNT THE BREATHS PER MINUTE SO I WOULD KNOW WHEN THEY WERE SLOWING DOWN.

AFTER THE HOUR WE MOVED MOTHER TO THE HOSPICE WING OF THE HOSPITAL. THIS WING HAD JUST OPENED A FEW MONTHS BEFORE. MATT LAUER, THE MORNING NEWSCASTER ON NBC HAD HELPED TO RAISE THE MONEY FOR THE HOSPICE WING BECAUSE WHEN HIS FATHER HAD BEEN IN THIS HOSPITAL DYING, THERE WAS NOT A HOSPICE WING AVAILABLE. IT WAS A BLESSING, AND I THANK MATT LAUER. HE CONTINUES TO RAISE MONEY FOR THIS HOSPICE WING YEARLY WITH A GOLF TOURNAMENT IN PALM BEACH. THIS IS TRULY A CASE OF ONE PERSON MAKING A HUGE DIFFERENCE IN MANY LIVES.

THE HOSPICE WING IS SO COMFORTING. THE BEDS HAVE HAND-KNITTED AFGANS. THERE ARE CD PLAYERS IN THE ROOMS. THERE ARE COMFORTABLE CHAIRS FOR THE FAMILY AND A ROOM WITH COFFEE AND SNACKS. IT FEELS LIKE A COMFORTABLE HOME, RATHER THAN A HOSPITAL AND THE STAFF FEELS LIKE FAMILY WITH THEIR SINCERE CARING.

THE CHAPLAIN CAME REGULARLY TO SEE MY MOTHER AND TO TALK WITH ME. THE MUSIC STAFF CAME AND PLAYED MUSIC TO MY MOTHER. ALL THE STAFF SAID I COULD CALL 24 HOURS SEVEN DAYS A WEEK IF I NEEDED TO DO SO. THEY WERE SO GENEROUS OF HEART. EVEN NOW AS I WRITE THIS I HAVE TEARS IN MY EYES. IT IS OVER TWO YEARS LATER, AND IT IS STILL HARD TO RELIVE ALL OF THIS. HOWEVER, HAVING A HOSPICE WING IN THE HOSPITAL WAS TRULY A BLESSING. THE STAFF CARED FOR MOTHER – AND THEY CARED FOR ME. AS I THINK BACK ON THIS THEY WERE TRULY "MOTHERING" ME, WRAPPING THEIR ARMS AND THOUGHTS AROUND ME AND BECOMING MY FAMILY WHILE I NEEDED THEM.

FINALLY MOTHER'S OWN DOCTOR CAME BACK. FORTUNATELY, SHE BELIEVES IN HOSPICE AND A GENTLE END OF LIFE, AND SHE CAME TO SEE MOTHER DAILY. SHE CALLED ME ONE MORNING TO TELL ME SHE HAD JUST BEEN TO SEE MOTHER AND THAT MOTHER HAD ACTUALLY RESPONDED TO SOME OF HER QUESTIONS. UP UNTIL THIS TIME MOTHER HAD BEEN IN WHAT I THOUGHT WAS A COMA. THE HOSPICE STAFF BELIEVES THAT THE LAST THING A PATIENT LOSES IS THEIR HEARING, EVEN IN A COMA STATE. AFTER MY EXPERIENCE I ALSO BELIEVE THIS. THE DOCTOR HAD ASKED MOTHER IF SHE WAS COMFORTABLE AND MOTHER MOANED, "I DON'T KNOW". TO THE DOCTOR'S QUESTION OF WHETHER SHE WAS IN PAIN MOTHER MOANED "NO".

WHEN I WENT TO SEE MOTHER LATER THAT DAY, I WAS PREPARED TO HAVE HER TALK SOME. WHEN THE NURSE AND I REARRANGED MOTHER'S PILLOWS, I ASKED HER IF SHE WAS MORE COMFORTABLE AND SHE MOANED, " I DON'T KNOW." HAD HER DOCTOR NOT TOLD ME EARLIER IN THE DAY THAT MOTHER HAD TALKED, I WOULD HAVE BEEN VERY SHOCKED. WHAT I LEARNED LATER WAS THAT IT IS NOT UNUSUAL FOR PATIENTS NEAR THE END OF LIFE TO HAVE A BIT OF A RALLY. IT CAN ACTUALLY SIGNAL THAT THEIR LIFE IS ALMOST OVER. AT THE TIME IT FELT VERY SURREAL, AS IF MOTHER HAD SOMEHOW COME BACK FROM ALREADY BEING DEAD. THIS EXPERIENCE WAS A LITTLE LIKE BEING WITH MOTHER WHEN SHE

HAD ALZHEIMER'S: THERE WAS ONE REALITY AND THEN THERE WAS A DIFFERENT REALITY.

THE NIGHT BEFORE MOTHER TALKED, I HAD TOLD MY BEST FRIEND KAREN THAT I WAS AMAZED THAT MOTHER WAS STILL HANGING ON. IT HAD BEEN FOUR DAYS SINCE WE HAD MOVED HER INTO THE HOSPICE WING. KAREN ASKED WHAT I HAD BEEN SAYING TO MOTHER. I TOLD HER I HAD BEEN TELLING MOTHER THAT SHE HAD TO LET GO AS DADDY AND MY SISTER WENDI WERE WAITING FOR HER. AS THE DAYS WENT ON I HAD TOLD HER THEY WERE WONDERING WHAT WAS TAKING HER SO LONG. I DID NOT WANT TO LOSE MY MOTHER, BUT I ALSO DID NOT WANT HER TO SUFFER ANY MORE.

KAREN IS SO WISE. SHE TOLD ME I HAD TO TELL MOTHER THAT I WOULD BE OK. THIS WOULD NEVER HAVE OCCURRED TO ME TO SAY. YET IT MADE SENSE. MOTHER WAS OFTEN ASKING ME WHO WOULD TAKE CARE OF ME SOMEDAY WHEN I WAS SICK. IF I WERE ABLE TO REASSURE HER THAT SHE DID NOT HAVE TO WORRY ABOUT ME, I FELT SURE SHE WOULD STOP FIGHTING TO STAY WITH ME.

SO THE NEXT MORNING I TOLD MOTHER THAT IT WAS OK TO LEAVE ME, AND THAT I WOULD BE OK.

THE FOLLOWING MORNING I HAD A CALL FROM THE HOSPICE NURSE THAT MOTHER HAD EXPIRED. OUR JOURNEY TO THE WORLD OF ALZHEIMER'S HAD ENDED.

CHAPTER SEVENTEEN
THE JOURNEY CONTINUES ALONE

ALTHOUGH WE WERE ON THE JOURNEY TOGETHER, IT OFTEN FELT THAT WE WERE TRAVELING ON DIFFERENT ROADS.

A FEW WEEKS BEFORE THE ONE YEAR ANNIVERSARY OF MOTHER'S DEATH, I FOUND MYSELF HAVING HEART ATTACK SYMPTOMS. IT WAS SUBTLE BUT IT WAS THERE. TWICE BEFORE IN MY LIFE WHEN I HAD BEEN UNDER GREAT STRESS, I HAD FELT THE SAME WAY. MY FATHER HAD HEART DISEASE, SO I NEVER IGNORE THESE SYMPTOMS. I WENT TO THE DOCTOR WHO TOOK MY SYMPTOMS SERIOUSLY. NOTHING WAS WRONG. I DID NOT REALIZE UNTIL AFTER THE ACTUAL ONE YEAR ANNIVERSARY OF MOTHER'S DEATH WHEN I WENT TO TEMPLE TO REMEMBER AND HONOR HER, HOW STRESSFUL THE ANTICIPATION OF THE ONE YEAR ANNIVERSARY WAS. I DON'T KNOW WHY ANY OF US ARE HOOKED INTO NUMBERS LIKE ONE YEAR. I DO KNOW THAT ONE YEAR SEEMS TO MAKE A DIFFERENCE. BIRTHDAYS AND ANNIVERSARIES MAY HAVE THE SAME EFFECT; THEY ARE MARKERS ON OUR ROAD OF LIFE.

EVEN TODAY THERE ARE GIFTS THAT MY MOTHER IS BESTOWING. WHEN I WAS LAST IN CLEVELAND I WAS IN THE LOCAL DELI AND SAW ONE OF MOTHER'S FRIENDS. THEY HAD KNOWN EACH OTHER SINCE CHILDHOOD AND I HAD KNOWN THIS WOMAN ALL MY LIFE. SHE TOLD ME THAT THE DAY OF THE FUNERAL SHE AND ANOTHER WOMAN HAD BEEN REUNITED AFTER MANY YEARS OF NOT SEEING EACH OTHER. THEY NOW MEET EVERY TUESDAY FOR DINNER AND REMINISCE, AND REMEMBER MOTHER. SHE SAID TO ME THAT SHE THINKS OF THIS RENEWED FRIENDSHIP AS A GIFT FROM MY MOTHER.

WHILE MOTHER WAS IN THE HOSPICE WING OF THE HOSPITAL I WAS IN THE ELEVATOR GOING UP TO HER ROOM. IN THE ELEVATOR WITH ME WAS AN OLDER GENTLEMAN WITH A CART FILLED WITH BOOKS AND MAGAZINES. I ASKED HIM WHERE THE HOSPITAL GETS THE BOOKS AND MAGAZINES. HE TOLD ME THEY ARE DONATED. SINCE THEN, AT LEAST TWICE A MONTH, I TAKE MY MAGAZINES TO THE HOSPITAL. THE ENTIRE STAFF AT THIS HOSPITAL WAS SO WONDERFUL AND CARING WHILE MOTHER WAS THERE. THIS IS A VERY SMALL PAYBACK. THIS IS ONE WAY I CONTINUE TO HONOR

MY MOTHER. I LIKE TO THINK OF IT AS A GIFT SHE IS GIVING TO THE HOSPITAL.

I AM STILL INVOLVED IN THE CLEVELAND CHAPTER OF THE ALZHEIMERS ASSOCIATION. RECENTLY, THROUGH THE FUND I SET UP IN MOTHER'S NAME, WE WERE ABLE TO PURCHASE TWO TAPES TO GIVE TO CAREGIVERS, BOTH BY BELLERUTH NAPARSTEK. ONE IS: MEDITATIONS TO RELIEVE STRESS. THE OTHER IS: AFFIRMATIONS FOR MIND, BODY AND SPIRIT. THE PACKAGING HAS A STICKER ON IT THAT READS: THIS GIFT MADE POSSIBLE THROUGH THE RUTH W. SILBERMAN FUND, ALZHEIMER'S ASSOCIATION CLEVELAND AREA CHAPTER (216-721-8457. MOTHER'S LIFE AND HER DEATH CONTINUE TO TOUCH OTHERS, AND FOR THAT I AM GRATEFUL.

THESE MANY MONTHS LATER, THE PAIN OF LOSING MOTHER IS STILL INTENSE. HOWVER, I ALSO HAVE MANY MOMENTS OF JOY WHEN I LOOK AROUND MY HOUSE. I SEE MOTHER'S ARTWORK AND HER FURNITURE AS WELL AS MANY PHOTOS OF HER. I HAVE MANY GOOD MEMORIES OF HER. THOSE GOOD MEMORIES ARE WHAT I HOLD ONTO.

AS I FINISH WRITING THIS STORY I AM ABOUT TO GO TO CLEVELAND FOR A SUPPORT GROUP MEETING GIVEN BY THE ALZHEIMERS ASSOCIATION. THE ALZHEIMER PATIENTS ARE DOING A SERIES OF MEETINGS WHERE THEY ARE MAKING MEMORY BOXES. THIS PROJECT IS SPONSORED BY MY MOTHER'S FUND. THE ALZHEIMER PATIENTS ARE TAKING PHOTOS, CARDS AND VARIOUS MOMENTOS AND FASTENING COPIES TO WOODEN BOXES. ONCE THE OUTSIDE OF THE BOXES ARE COMPLETE, THE ACTUAL PHOTOS, ETC. CAN BE PUT INTO THE BOXES. WHEN THE ALZHEIMER PATIENTS NEED TO GO TO THE PAST, THE BOXES WILL BE READY FOR THEM. WHEN THEY ARE DEPRESSED OR AGGITATED, THEIR CAREGIVERS CAN TAKE OUT THE BOXES AND TRY TO ENGAGE THEM IN OLD MEMORIES. I AM SO PROUD TO BE PART OF THIS PROJECT.

RECENTLY I SAW A PAID PROGRAM ON TELEVISION THAT AN ASSISTED LIVING FACILITY HAD PRODUCED. MEMORY BOXES WITH PHOTOS OF "THE TENANTS' LOVED ONES ARE HUNG ON THE WALL NEAR THE APARTMENT DOOR ENTRANCE. THIS VERSION OF A MEMORY BOX ALSO CAN BE EFFECTIVE. PERHAPS YOU WOULD LIKE TO HELP YOUR ALZHEIMER PERSON MAKE A MEMORY BOX. WHEN YOU DO, I HOPE YOU THINK OF MY MOTHER.

WHEN MOTHER WAS TRAVELING THROUGH ALZHEIMER'S, IT BECAME

THE COUNTRY OF HER IMAGINATION. HER REALITY AND MY REALITY WERE OFTEN NOT THE SAME. ALTHOUGH WE WERE ON THE JOURNEY TOGETHER, IT OFTEN FELT THAT WE WERE TRAVELING ON DIFFERENT ROADS. AS YOU GO THROUGH YOUR OWN JOURNEY WITH YOUR FAMILY I WISH YOU SAFE TRAVELS. YOUR TRIP WILL BE DIFFERENT THAN MINE WAS WITH MY MOTHER, BUT I HOPE BY SHARING OUR TRIP WITH YOU, IT WILL MAKE YOURS A LITTLE BIT EASIER AND A LITTLE BIT BETTER.